The Celtic School of Yoga
An Aisling for the 21st Century

Aisling (nf: Celtic; Irish) ~ **Vision; Dream**

Uma Dinsmore-Tulli PhD   Jack Harrison MA FAHI

First published in 2015 by

The Celtic School of Yoga

Cloosh

Kinvara

County Galway

Ireland

www.thecelticschoolofyoga.com

British Library Cataloguing in Publication Data

Dinsmore-Tuli, Uma and Harrison, Jack.

The Celtic School of Yoga: An Aisling for the 21st Century

1.Yoga—Philosophy. 2. Celtic studies—Spirituality. 3. Ireland

ISBN number 978-0-9934200-0-9

Design JHA

Typeset in ITC Garamond

Printed in Ireland by Walsh Colour Print

Acknowledgements

Thanksgiving is celebrated as an exalted spiritual practice, both in the teachings of yoga, and in the wisdom of the Celtic world. Giving thanks gladdens the heart: so it is a pleasure for us to honour the assistance and inspiration that has been given to us by all of the many people and places that have helped create this book. Our first debt of thanks is to Trea and Kevin Heapes at PureCamping eco campsite in Querrin, for hosting the Santosa Yoga Camp, where the seeds of this book were sown. We also express our deep appreciation for all the yogis and yoginis at Santosa Yoga Camps in Glastonbury and Querrin who gave such an open-hearted welcome to the teachings of the Celtic School of Yoga.

Jack thanks:

Alice, Katy and Jamie Harrison for my total astonishment at their very existence, Ann Lu for inspiration, Bairbre Ní Fhlionn for long friendship, Benita Galván for her joy of life, Dorien and David for love, Conor Newman for scholarship, Emil Wendl for philosophy in the sun, Gabriel Rosenstock for poetry, Gyanmurti Mark Johnston for incisive comments and suggestions, John Friend for heart-centred teaching, Kitty McCabe for carrying me in my early life, Laragh and David Cunningham for boundless enthusiasm, Lorraine Cf Pulchellum and Christine Stewart for Inishboffin and songbirds, Mallika McCarthy for love and photographs, Mari Kennedy for reminding me of lost genius, Maria Pforr for reminding me of the Moon, Michael Ryan for brotherhood, Paul Dallaghan for re-awakening music, Sianna Sherman for being my muse, Terri Russell for standing by me, Ray Boyce and Sean Reynolds for helping to put it all together and all the poets and photographers and artists who unveil the world.

Uma thanks:

Adrienne Egan for knowing what I was on about and playing the bodhrán for Hanuman in the Burren, Alexandra Pope for helping me see I wasn't mad, Amanda Brown for deep affimation at Buddhafield, Angela Clare Brew for sharing my delight and holding Santosa steady, Angela Farmer and Victor Van Kooten for providing a spacious retreat time to gestate the hidden lineage of Celtic Yoga, Ben Jarlett, Mami Sayo, Alison Fairchild for proofing, Christopher Gladwell for gracious presence and crystal clear teachings, Colette Nolan for convincing me to come home to Ireland and not go to India again, Cryn Horn for assurance and cracking proof-reading, Danielle Jones for shining her light and being the best ever Santosa toilet faery, Dave Brocklebank for inviting me to share yoga in the Burren Yoga centre, and for some beautiful images, my brother David Moore for many gorgeous Burren photographs, Diarmaid Ferriter for time and attention, Eileen Heneghan for perfect hospitality in Cashel, Elizabeth Stanley at Yogacampus and The Life Centre for welcoming the teachings of the Celtic School of Yoga to London, Graham Burns for continued patient academic support, Habiba Willow for being the Hafiz-loving faery at the bottom of my garden, Jason Birch and Jacqui Hargreaves

for scholarly insight on the real history of Yoga Nidra, Lavina Faleiro O'Farrell for knowing that now was the right time, Laura Tonello for sisterly insights, Matthew Remski for showing up in the Cotswolds at the perfect moment and asking difficult questions, my husband Nirlipta Tuli for putting up with endless enthusiasms, Sinead Barratt for a home in Ennistymon, and Sivani Mata for loving Lalla and keeping up with the newsletters when I was distracted. Lastly I thank my patient children Prayaag Eileen, Abhisheka, and Tejomaya Dinsmore-Tuli for not minding that their mother was not paying them any proper attention (again).

We are glad to express our gratitude to all of these beings. For any mistakes, omissions or oversights that remain, we have no one to thank but ourselves.

Permissions

Photo Credits

Contents

Preface

This book was written in many places—from the fertile rock of the Burren in County Clare, to the Greek island of Lesvos, to the Heavens of Stroud in the Cotswold Hills. The seeds for it were planted in 2013 when Uma and Jack met at the Irish Santosa Yoga Camp in a converted cowshed on the river Shannon. Discovering a shared vision, the authors have been delighted to collaborate in nurturing the Celtic School of Yoga.

The School—in its meaning of a shared philosophy—represents a new paradigm in the sharing of yoga that is rooted in the nourishing earth of our own islands and their spiritual heritage. Our vision is to begin to re-connect a resonance heard at the Irish side of the Indo-European linguistic area, to that of the sub-continent of India; to help people in the Western world to realise that our yoga—our connection with the Earth, the Sun, and the Moon—is not the exclusive territory of a far-Eastern tradition but rather it sings inside ourselves, inspired by our own tradition and our own place in the world.

There has been much controversy over the use of the word Celtic and whether it actually describes any kind of ethnicity at all. It is absolutely clear that there exists a group of Celtic languages, a Celtic artistic spirit, and arguably a Celtic temperament. Of course, none of these things are definitive or easy to see; in a way this uncertainty or elusiveness is a fundamental characteristic of the word Celtic—it is interesting to observe that the Irish term *faoi cheilt* means "hidden" or "underground".

While we understand fully the difficulties associated with the term Celtic, we have chosen to use it because, for us, it brings together a series of disparate impressions—such as an understanding of the transformative power of language, music and the natural world, and a central honouring of the power of the deep feminine—which extends even into the modern era.

In the Celtic tradition, it is widely held that the usually solid boundaries between worlds and dimensions dissolve at pivotal points of the year such as *Bealtaine* (May Day) and *Samhain* (Halloween). Part of our intention for this Celtic School of Yoga is to help to dissolve the boundaries between Ireland and India, the boundaries between women and men, and the boundaries that separate us from our natural yoga.

Through the practice of yoga we awaken our bodies and minds to the amazing reality, the pure joy, of living in the natural world.

It is so easy to forget the astonishing mystery of just being here.

Uma Dinsmore-Tuli and Jack Harrison
Samhain 2015

Truly we live with mysteries too marvellous to be understood…

Let me keep my distance, always, from

Those who think they have the answers.

Let me keep company always with those who say

"Look!" and laugh in astonishment, and bow their heads.

Mary Oliver

Foreword

The Quest

They said: "She dwelleth in some place apart,
Immortal Truth, within whose eyes
Who looks may find the secret of the skies
And healing for life's smart!"

I sought Her in loud caverns underground,
On heights where lightnings flashed and fell;
I scaled high Heaven; I stormed the gates of Hell,
But Her I never found

Till thro' the tumults of my Quest I caught
A whisper: "Here, within thy heart,
I dwell; for I am thou: behold, thou art
The Seeker—and the Sought."

An Cuardach

Ar siad: "Ta cónaí uirthi i bhfad i gcéin
An Fhírinne Shíoraí, agus ina súil
Tá mistéir uile na ndúl
Dóibh siúd atá i bpéin."

Lorgaíos i bpluaiseanna glóracha Í
Is fós sa tintreach i measc na mbeann
Dhreapas go neamh is sheas ar leac na bpian,
Ach ní raibh Sí ann

Go dtí gur thug mo Chuardach mé
Go ciúin faoi dhéin mo chroí:
"Anseo atáim, ionatsa féin
Go brách is go síoraí!"

James H. Cousins; Irish translation: Gabriel Rosenstock

James Cousins (1873–1956), Irish literary figure who lived and died in India. He had a profound influence on one of India's greatest yogis, Sri Aurobindo.

Introduction—Why this Book Now?

We live in a time when the need for respite is often desperate, and there is deep disconnection from home, land and Self. The yoga in this book is a vision of how we might heal this disconnection by experiencing the sweetness of being welcomed home to ourselves, by savouring the health and vitality that comes from being well-rooted, and by inviting the joy of living into our lives.

Many people are adrift and rootless, working long hours to service heavy debts, driven by relentless pressures of constant availability, processing vast amounts of data, and so profoundly exhausted they barely know who they are. Many are lost and confused, unable to sleep or digest their food, tired and frustrated, depressed and dissatisfied. Insomnia, anxiety and depression, sexual difficulties, infertility, eating disorders and many other everyday human miseries everywhere limit our capacity for happiness. All of these sufferings are signs of being disconnected from the physical body, or so deeply troubled by it that there is little joy to be had in being alive at all.

The practice of yoga is not just physical exercise or controlled breathing. It is a technique to reconnect us to our source of life so we can sustain our vitality and serenity and build our potential for joyful living. This is the point of the teachings of the Celtic School of Yoga.

Yoga is, for us, a set of powerful tools and techniques to support self-care, nurture, exploration and delight. The practice of yoga supports our well-being, boosts vitality, strengthens our immune system, helps us sleep, digest, and think more effectively, and empowers us to relate with compassion and kindness to each other. Yoga practices support menstrual health, reproductive function and recovery from injury and illness. The meditative breath and movement work of yoga enables people to self-regulate, to manage stress, to make wise choices about what nourishes them, to reduce anxiety and depression and to cultivate joy and delight in life.

And while yoga is a positive support for health, vitality and joy, if we believe that it comes from India alone, then it can seem to Westerners that we need to look very far afield to find in other cultures what we need to live our lives.

The intention of all the practices, stories and ideas shared in this book is to empower you to trust your own inner teacher, to discover how it might feel to be truly nourished by a yoga that is appropriate to your own place and land and time.
In the pages of this book we show how any yoga which helps you to re-connect to the land in which you are planted, or which builds a nourishing connection to the stories and traditions that nourished your ancestral lines, will be a yoga practice that sustains your capacity for joyful living.

1 An Aisling for the 21st Century

This is a vision (an *aisling*) for a yoga of enchantment—the process of singing a place or state or idea into existence.

When these places, states or ideas are called into being through voice and breath, they can be embodied within a life-affirming yoga practice that brings us home to ourselves. This is the deep hospitality of re-connection.

Celtic Yoga invites you to rediscover a life that is nourished in a very practical sense by the spiritual wisdom of the Celtic world; a life in which everything is celebrated as sacred—each breath, each movement, each feeling of heart, is welcomed into this yoga of homecoming. To practise Celtic Yoga is to be fully rooted in the earth and enraptured by life. Celtic Yoga *en-chants* us; it calls us to be fully alive and in deep connection with the land, and with the stories and poetic traditions that grew from her.

Western *yoginis* and *yogis* have always looked to India to discover yoga, often without realising that its essence is intrinsic to our own culture and is dramatically alive at our far Western boundaries. Enchantment welcomes us back home to ourselves and links the Eastern and Western inspirational edges of our yoga practice, our connecting practice.

The purpose of this Celtic School of Yoga is to re-establish a balance between East and West, between what we look for outside of ourselves and what we find when we come home. This creative reconciliation is also a return to a balance between the deep feminine, and the masculine principles that have preserved yoga practice for so long.

The creative Wisdom of all things has established marvellous and ineffable harmonies by which all things come together in a concord or friendship or peace or love or however else the union of all things can be designated.

Johannes Scotus,
9th century Irish Philosopher

Until the Battle of the Boyne, Ireland belonged to Asia.

WB Yeats

Newgrange (Brú na Bóinne), the birthplace of the God of Love, Music and Poetry whose mother was BoVinda, goddess of the White Cow.

Aisling Gheal—A Bright Vision

The Celtic School of Yoga has its heart at the Western edge of Europe, the boundary of the ancient World, and is inspired by the Bardic Law and Philosophy Schools of old Ireland. The Irish Bardic Order was said to be old when St Patrick arrived in the 5th Century AD. Its function was to teach poetry and associated arts, and it is likely that the order had its origins in the pre-Christian, and perhaps even pre-Celtic, era of goddess worship in Ireland. This was the age of the White Goddess described by the poet Robert Graves, when he said: "True poetry (inspired by the Muse and her prime symbol, the Moon) even today is a survival, or intuitive re-creation, of ancient Goddess-worship".

Having existed for thousands of years, the schools were mostly driven underground in the 17th century as a result of penal laws and a series of plantations of people into Ireland.

The traditions of the Bardic Schools lie deep in the land, nourished by a connection with the cycles of nature and an honouring of the earth herself. The Celtic School of Yoga is rooted in the same land that nurtured these traditions, and its teachings are a twenty-first century re-flowering of the poetry and philosophical debate which the Bardic Schools fostered. One of the poetic forms taught at the schools was the *Aisling*, a poem dedicated to re-forming the connection with the old order. The word refers to a mystical vision where the land of Ireland is represented as a beautiful woman.

Our *Aisling Gheal*—our Bright Vision—for the school is to celebrate a yoga practice which reconnects with the principles of the Bardic Schools; a practice which has been developed from the ground up rather than as part of a top-down hierarchy; which connects the practical, spiritual wisdom of the Celtic world with everything we have learnt from yoga. To do this means allowing our *asana*, *pranayama*, poetry, music and meditative practice to express the dance between the sun, the earth, and the moon, and so to rediscover the true rapture of living.

Oh, what a catastrophe for man when he cut himself off from the rhythm of the year, from his unison with the sun and the earth. Oh, what a catastrophe, what a maiming of love, when it was made a personal, merely personal feeling, taken away from the rising and the setting of the sun, and cut off from the magic connection of the solstice and the equinox! This is what is the matter with us. We are bleeding at the roots because we are cut off from the Earth and Sun and Stars.

D H Lawrence

The sexual liaison between the sovereignty goddess and the hero reconciles the masculine principle of order with the sometimes contradictory but properly complementary feminine principle of fertility and abundance.

Louis de Paor

The Entrance Stone at Newgrange decorated with what may be symbols of the sun. Above is the "roof box" where the sun shines through into the chamber only at the mid-winter solstice.

The connection of the Celtic world with yoga is that both Ireland and India are on the peripheries of the great Indo-European expansion. Through cultural expansions like this, ancient modes of thought, ways of being and other cultural elements are often preserved at the peripheries. Inspired by this realisation we seek to re-establish Celtic and pre-Celtic mythology, poetry and story-telling as the foundation for a modern school of yoga—a natural and indigenous expression of the experience of yoga in our culture. This is a reconnection of one edge of the Indo-European expression to the other.

Though Indian yoga has been, and continues to be, a great inspiration to us, we have learned that we can root our yoga practice in our own Celtic and pre-Celtic mythology while continuing to practise techniques learnt from India, which themselves have often been inspired by, or perfected in, the West. This means that we can practise and develop our yoga on the solid and familiar foundation of our own traditions of knowledge, art, music, poetry and philosophy.

Proto-Shiva as "lord of the animals" from a seal found at Mohenjo-daro in Pakistan, one of the largest settlements of the Indus Valley civilisation.

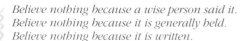

Believe nothing because a wise person said it.
Believe nothing because it is generally held.
Believe nothing because it is written.
Believe nothing because it is said to be divine.
Believe nothing because someone else believes it.
But believe only what you yourself judge to be true.

Gautama Buddha, Kalama Sutta

A plate from a Celtic cauldron found in Gundestrup, Denmark. It shows a horned figure holding a serpent and what is probably a gold torc. He is surrounded by animal arrangements that are remarkably similar to the "Shiva" seal above.

A New Paradigm in Sharing Yoga

We see this as a school of philosophy or thought where we move in the same direction with independence and strength rooted in our own minds, hearts and land, rather than in any learned belief. It is a place of discovery and rediscovery of the wisdom, wonder and rapture of daily life.

Though this is a new paradigm, it is rooted in the very beginnings of yoga as a spiritual practice entirely founded on a deep connection, a *yoga*, with the living Earth.

All yoga schools have a philosophical underpinning, and most today are based on the marvellous, tangled, deep spirituality of the Indian sub-continent. The myths and stories of Shiva, Shakti, Lakshmi, and Krishna and the philosophical reflections that we learn from the *Vedas*, *Upanishads* and *Tantras*, give us the inspiration and structure within which to place our yoga practices.

But fundamentally these are not gods and goddesses living on some cloud or temple in Varanasi or Rishikesh; they are expressions of our human dreams—which themselves are expressions of divinity—and their function is to bring us back to our place as humans in the dance of the Earth and the Sun, to the dew-wet grass of the morning with the light on her face, and ultimately to let us know that we are a living part of this vital dance.

But what if we, as Westerners, do not have to look to India for inspiration? What if we realise that the Gods and Goddesses of the Celtic and pre-Celtic pantheon are still very much alive and active in Ireland and other parts of the Celtic world? What if we realise that, in many cases, the universal dreams which make up the foundation of our practice are variants of stories which have been with us all our lives? Even if we have never heard these stories, they have shaped the minds and hearts of our fathers and mothers. Because they have lived within us and our parents, and our parents' parents, for so long, perhaps we feel their presence more closely and more intimately?

The world will never starve for want of wonders, but only for want of wonder.
GK Chesterton

A whole people, a whole civilisation, immeasurably strange to us…and yet we are not moved because of its strangeness, but because we have met our own image.
WB Yeats, writing about the Indian poet Rabindranath Tagore

This is a vision for a living yoga that seeks to bring rapture back into our lives, supported by the power we gain by owning our practice ourselves and by rooting this practice in our land. It is held by a questioning intelligence—where does our yoga vision come from? Does it not arise in the West as much as in the East? Can our own stories not be as much a basis for a real living yoga as the stories we hear from the other side of the world?

The Bright Vision (*Aisling Gheal*) is to create a balance which makes it possible to take our yoga back to our own roots and yet realise that it is this very activity which brings us closer to our brothers and sisters in India. They are not repositories of something for which we need to seek; they are us and we are them, and our dreams and stories are the same.

One of the difficulties of importing to northern countries a purely traditional Indian approach to yoga is that the climate and cultural milieu are so very different; what may feel natural and easy to practise at four in the morning in the tropics in January, feels like torture in November on the West coast of Ireland, or on a desperately cold February afternoon in Somerset.

Things are different here. Seasonal changes in available light and heat shape our lives according to where we live. Insistence on rigid structures or schedules of practice imported from India, and/or upon an authoritarian scheme of teaching that demands long periods of retreat in ashrams, is not always appropriate, possible, or nourishing for us. When we attempt to adhere to Indian systems and schedules of yoga practice we can become depleted, frustrated, or disheartened because these methods and rhythms simply do not fit with our lived experience. We need a new way to share yoga so that it nourishes everyone.

The sharing of yoga through the Celtic School of Yoga is responsive, subtle and intelligently attuned to the rhythms of our lives here and now.

Why are you unhappy? Because 99.9 percent of everything you think, and of everything you do, is for yourself—and there isn't one.

Wei Wu Wei (Irish writer, Terence Gray, 1895–1986)

When Fionn and the Fianna lived
They loved the hills, not hermit-cells.
Blackbird speech is what they loved
Not the sound, unlovely, of your bells.

Beautiful Blackbird of Doire and Chairn, 15th Century

Patrick, you chatter too loud and lift your crosier too high,
Your stick would be kindling soon if my son Osgar stood by.

Scél Lemm Dúib, 9th century

Monastery of the Archangel,
Sceilig Mhichil, Co Kerry

2 The Indo-European Connection

Inspiring our Bright Vision are the clear similarities we find when we compare Celtic myth, poetry and images with those from the world of yoga. These resonances may be the result of a continuing connection within the Indo-European family which have been preserved at the edges of the expansion, or they may be the result of later connections.

The images of Shiva on the Mohenjo Daro tablets and that of the Celtic Cernunnos on the Gundestrup Cauldron with their horned gods, lotus postures and surrounding animals are astonishingly similiar; the structure, form and tone of the Irish creation myth, the *Song of Aimhirghin*, about the poet who sang Ireland into existence (his name may be the origin of the modern Irish word for a song) has, as Yeats observed, a striking similarity to the Indian philosophical reflections presented in the *Upanishads*; the Irish Mother goddess and the Indian primordial water goddess were both called Danu.

At the great Neolithic cathedral at Newgrange we can see the celebration of the dance of Shiva and Shakti—the Sun and the Earth—acting itself out as the midwinter sunlight shines up the passage to bring the inner chamber, and the whole dark world, back to life. Nearby the collection of Neolithic tombs called *Sliabh na Caillí* (Sleeve na Kali—the Hill of the Witch goddess) evoke the name of Kali, the Indian dark mother of time and change. Aonghus of the *Tuatha Dé Danann* (the people of Danu) who is the Celtic god of Love, Music and Poetry can be seen as the Celtic Krishna. His mother, the water goddess, called BoVinda (the White Cow goddess), is again redolent of Krishna.

The writings of the French philologist Georges Dumézil suggest a connection between the Irish queen/goddess Medb and the beautiful Madhavi of the Indian epic story the *Mahabharata*. Madhavi was the goddess of Fertility and Kingship and is also associated with mead and intoxication. *Madhu* in Sanskrit means "honey" or "sweet drink". "Medb" may also mean "she who intoxicates". There are several European Celtic tombs of women in which have been found pottery or metal containers with the remains of an alcoholic drink based on honey. Brighid's Crosses, made of woven rushes to celebrate Brighid, the goddess of the Spring, on the first day of February, are often made, not in the form of a cross, but in the form of a swastika, a symbol of auspiciousness (the decorative use of which in India and Ireland predates the Nazi swastika

"Fasting on someone" conducting a personal hunger strike, outside the house of someone who has insulted you, is a practice common to both Ireland and India.

Myles Dillon

(There is in Ireland)…evidence for a sacred marriage with a goddess whose name and association with a sacramental drink has Indo-European roots.

John Waddell

Many westerners have turned to India for the study of Tantra and kundalini power, because it was here the ancient techniques have been most completely retained. Was there ever anything like them in the West, indigenous to Western people? The answer is yes, because the same Goddess ruled all. The Dravidian [South Indian] Danu was the Irish Danu. The Indian Kali was the Irish Cailleach…

Monica Sjöö and Barbara Mor

by several thousand years). *Swa-stika* means well-being in Sanskrit. Horses were very important in early Indo-European society and the ancient Indic horse-sacrificing ritual of *asvamedha* has detailed similarities to the horse-sacrificing rituals of the ancient Irish.

There are also resonances between the origin stories of Vishnu and the great Irish hero Fionn. In the mythology of India, Vishnu came from the world ocean as a fish and child at once and was "radiant with the lustre of wisdom"; Fionn was born of the river goddess Bóinn to become a Seer/Druid. He emerged out of the river Boyne bringing with him all the *Imbass* (wisdom) from the nine hazel trees which grew at her source.

These are just a few examples. There are many more that connect so directly to the living spirit of yoga that they cast a new light on our practice. We are not in any way trying to replace the stories from India in our yoga practice. We are rather trying to show how the poetics and philosophy of yoga are as much present in our own communal memories, and connection with the land, as they are in those of the Indian people. The stories and poems nourish a heart-centred and Earth-honouring practice of Yoga awareness that embodies the realities of our lives.

If we listen to these echoes we hear the voices of true *yogis* and *yoginis* who cherish the deep magic of yoga tantra in the West. These *yogis* and *yoginis* are the hidden lineage of a Celtic approach to yoga. This is not the yoga of *swamis* and patriarchal institutions, nor of ersatz yoga academies of hierarchical control, nor authoritarian teachers. It is the yoga of poets, philosophers and radical political activists whose hearts and souls are inspired by their own Celtic heritage as well as by the teachings of the *Upanishads*, the Yoga *Sutras*, and the *Mahabharata*. These people planted the living spirit of yoga into their own Western lives and inspire the living practice of Celtic Yoga.

At the very end of his life, this same yearning for the peace of spiritual union, the yoga of reconnection, inspired an elderly Yeats to devote much of his time and energy to Indian philosophy.

The Oseberg Viking Ship "Buddha" with Celtic designs —probably an import to Norway from Ireland.

The correspondences drawn between early Ireland and Vedic India, the two geographical extremes of the Indo European world, have not gone unquestioned. But the cumulative evidence that Irish tradition retains Indo European characteristics lost or feebly reflected elsewhere in the west is impressive. These include horse sacrifice, those elements of sacral kingship such as the concept of the "prince's truth" (akin to the Hindu "Act of Truth" Satyakriya) and the recognition of the Indo European theme "the single sin of the sovereign".

John Waddell

Searching for Summer Swans   *Jack*

Around the year of the Millennium, I spent much of my time working on the exhibition at Brú na Bóinne, the Valley of the Boyne (BoVinda). I became fascinated by the archaeology and mythology of the great stone cathedral of Newgrange, as Professor Gabriel Cooney, who was working with me at the time, called it. One of the stories about the site was that Aonghus, Son of Youth, the Celtic cognate of Krishna, was born there. His mother was the goddess of the river and his father the great Sun god. Aonghus was the God of Love, Music and Poetry. When he grew up he fell in love with a beautiful girl called Caer who, as Yeats intimated, "faded into the brightening air" and could not be found, though Aonghus, and his father and mother, looked for her everywhere.

One day he was told that she had been turned into a swan and that he had to search for her somewhere in the West of Ireland; if he could recognise her in the flock, she would come back to him. The God of Love had lost his beloved and was to spend the rest of his life wandering Ireland looking for his beautiful swan.

Around the same time I became interested in astronomy. One evening in late Spring I turned to my star guide-book to see what constellations I should look for at that time of year. Following the instructions of my book, I went outside to a cold, star-lit night and looked to the south. There, just above the horizon was the constellation Cygnus, a giant starry swan, flying towards me, spanning the whole of the southern sky with her wings. I still remember the deep breath I took when I saw her.

To astronomers, Cygnus is the herald of Summer. To me it was Aonghus, lord of light but born in the darkness of the winter solstice, searching for the swan that signals the return of light to Ireland.

Swans on the River Boyne at Newgrange

I am a Wind Across the Sea

I am a Dewdrop let fall from the Sun

I am a Fire on every hill

I am a Shield over every head

Who but I is the tree and the lightning that strikes it?

Who but I is the dark secret of the dolmen not yet hewn?

Who knows the currents of the Moon?

Who knows the path of the Sun?

From The Song of Aimhirghin

The Self is the sun shining in the sky

The wind blowing in space

He is the fire at the altar

And in the home the guest…

He is the fish born in water

The plant growing in the Earth

The river flowing down from the mountain.

Katha Upanishad, II.2.2

WB Yeats, the Upanishads and Aimhirgin's Song.

When he was in his seventies, sick and tired, in the "interstices left by a long illness", Yeats travelled to Spain for a writing retreat with an Indian renunciate, Sri Purohit Swami. The two had first met in 1931, when Yeats was sixty-six. Between then and his death in 1939, Yeats devoted much time and energy to Indian philosophy, supporting Purohit Swami by writing introductions to five of his books, including his translation of Patanjali's *Yoga Sutra* in 1938.

So inspired was Yeats by the Swami's teachings, that he proposed to Sri Purohit that they travel together to India, to work on their translation of the *Upanishads*; but lack of money and Yeats's ill-health prevented this, and so they went to Majorca instead. There, just a few years before Yeats died, they completed their version of the principal *Upanishads* in English, in a translation that Yeats intended to read "as though the original had been written in common English".

Yeats recognised in Sri Purohit Swami a man who "knew what he was writing about" from deep personal experience. He supported Purohit's writings because, as a self-identified "old man in a hurry", the ageing poet felt an urgency to share the Indian philosophies he so admired. Yeats had an insight that *The Song of Aimhirghin*, which he called "the one fragment of pagan Irish philosophy come down", seemed "Asiatic" to him.

Of course it's not Asiatic at all, it's Irish, but to Yeats, the word was a way of describing something that was strange and yet familiar, part of a philosophy that had nourished his heart since his youth. Two years before he died, Yeats said that he had "fed on the *Upanishads* all his life"; for him what was "Asiatic'" was a deeply sustaining wisdom for living. And so, in his introduction to the *Upanishads* he wrote:

> "… when we turn towards the East… we are turning not less to the ancient West and North… our genuflections discover in that East something ancestral in ourselves."

Perhaps what Yeats really meant by his "Irish equals Asiatic" equation was that this *Song of Aimhirghin* was "yogic", and that Aimhirghin was the first Irish yogi. To understand this is to feel the "deep ancestral" pull that Yeats felt when he read the *Upanishads*, and to feel the connection between the spirit of the Indian philosophy he loved so passionately as an old man, and the Irish poetry and myths that had had him enchanted since his youth. Indeed, when Yeats first read Purohit Swami's book about his pilgrimage to the holy mountain of Kailas, the poet declared that it was the book he had been "waiting for since he was seventeen years old".

In his poetic imaginings, Yeats lived his whole life as a Celtic yogi, but it was only in his final eight years, during his creative and philosophical collaborations with Sri Purohit Swami, that he most clearly articulated the resonance between the spiritual wisdom of the Celtic world and the heart of yogic philosophies: "I am an old man with a poor memory… and nothing in my head but the *Aphorisms of Patanjali* and the novels of Balzac… When I read the travels of Purohit Swami … I am among familiar things."

A Burren Prayer

Oremus,
Maria de Petra Fertilis:

May the praise of rain on stone,
Recall the child lost in the heart's catacomb.

May the light that turns the limestone white
Remind us that our solitude is bright.

May the arrival of gentians in their blue surprise
Bring glimpses of delight to our eyes.

May the wells that dream in the stone
Soothe the eternal that sleeps in our bone.

May the contemplative mind of the mountain
Assure us that nothing is lost or forgotten.

May the antiphon of ocean on stone
Guide the waves of loneliness home.

May the spirits who dwell in the ruin of Corcomroe
Lead our hearts to the one who is beautiful to know.

Go maire na mairbh agus a mbrionglóidí
*I bhfoscadh chaoin dílis na Trinóide.**

> ** May the departed and their dreams*
> *Ever dwell in the kind and faithful shelter of*
> *the Trinity.*

John O'Donohue

3 Sacred Space

Ireland is a *palimpsest*, a series of layers, of sacred spaces from many different eras such as Early Christian monasteries, Round Towers, Megalithic monuments, and the countless holy wells and hermitages which are remnants of Celtic and pre-Celtic ways of seeing the world as the body of the Goddess herself.

The presence of these sites informs our yoga. They are physical manifestations or expressions in the landscape of the principles upon which our practice is based. These spaces are inspirations and guides that help us to heighten our yogic awareness. Connecting with these places helps us feel at home wherever we find ourselves in the world. This is first embodied and then voiced through the process of singing a place, or a state, or a feeling into existence (*en-chanting* it) using music and poetry, such as once happened with the almost lost place-names of Ireland.

In yoga practice, we can perceive the body as a sacred space in which there are many different dimensions. These are our inner worlds which can be visited in the same way as the heroes of the Celtic stories visit the other world by entering into sacred spaces like Newgrange to bring back the "fruits of Summer". In *yoga nidra* for example, we can experience, even in the depths of winter, the warmth and heat of an inner springtime as a physical reality.

The word "spiritual" has come to acquire connotations of "other worldly". And yet, for the practitioner, as distinct from the believer, the body can be experienced as a sacred space through a conscious practice based firmly in the reality of the earthly energy and wisdom. The great task is not to experience God as something extraneous, but to experience our own living reality, with body, mind and feelings open to the world and in touch with each other. The French philosopher and Jesuit priest, Teilhard de Chardin, believed that there is a place, a dimension, where everything is one.

The place we converge is where peace and the sensual, Buddha and Zorba, co-exist. Relationship itself is a sacred space in which peace and passion meet. Being human, the play of peace and passion is the sacred space in which we live.

Time and again, the digging of pits, shafts and ditches, and material offerings placed in the Earth or in watery places, appear to testify to an interest in those chtonic powers that had an impact on human affairs.

John Waddell

The Otherworld was an element of Indo-European belief and was a fluid concept that took various forms. In Ireland, it was seen as a prosperous and peaceful land, the dwelling place of malevolent creatures, a land of the dead, and a mirror world that might provide the outer world in winter with wild garlic and primroses and buttercups, the "fruits of summer".

John Waddell

I am a materialist-spiritualist...I teach a sensuous religion. I want Gautam the Buddha and Zorba the Greek to come closer and closer, my disciple has to be Zorba the Buddha. Man is body-soul together. Both have to be satisfied.

Osho

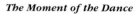

The Moment of the Dance

Aengus Óg, the sun-god of light, music and poetry, was conceived and born on the same day in Newgrange, in the temple to the womb of the mother Earth. The entrance and passage are aligned so that, only on the Winter Solstice, sunlight enters the inner chamber.

Home as a Sacred Space
Yeats, Tagore and Celtic Yoga

In 1912 Yeats was given an English translation of the Bengali poet Rabrindranath Tagore's *Gitanjali*. He was so deeply moved that it he couldn't put it down; it made him almost weep in public: "I have carried the manuscript about with me for days, reading it in railway trains, or in the top of omnibuses and I have often had to close it lest some stranger would see how much it moved me."

What was it about these Indian poems that made Yeats confess "they stirred my blood as nothing has for years". Why did Yeats love these Bengali lyrics so intensely? And what has this to do with Celtic Yoga?

Perhaps Yeats felt as if Tagore's poems brought him home. He felt an intimacy with the spirit of what Tagore shared; it was a recognition that, all his life, he had been seeking to reconnect with the deep rootedness in ancestral lands and culture that he could feel had nourished Tagore's poetic sensibilities. The poems, he reflected:

> "… display in their thought a world I have dreamed of all my life long. The work of a supreme culture, they yet appear as much the growth of the common soul as the grass and the rushes. A tradition, where poetry and religion are the same thing."

Yeats's tears over Tagore come from the same sadness he experienced in London, a quarter of a century previously, when, as a homesick twenty-three year old, he paused by a fountain in the Strand. There he felt a yearning for his boyhood Sligo, and a nostalgic recollection of his adolescent desire to live like the yogi Thoreau which inspired The "Lake Isle of Innisfree". At both these times in London, Yeats voiced a deep desire for a living connection to an indigenous spiritual wisdom: the sacred space of home.

The traces of Yeats's tears inspire Celtic yoga, because there is, in his passion for Tagore, also an implicit regret. They are tears of regret; he yearns to root his poetic rapture in a living spiritual tradition, but his roots are not so deeply planted as Tagore's. He moves between Ireland and England. Yeats is an Irish poet weeping in London; he sheds his tears for Tagore on English buses and in English streets. He writes the introduction to *Gitanjali* in London, in the same city where his own experience of deracination and yearning for Ireland inspired his youthful "Lake Isle of Innisfree" in 1888. He is not at home.

And Yeats knows that even had he been at home, there would have been no warm welcome for the poetic connection to indigenous spiritual wisdom that he so craves; he recognises it in Tagore because he so wants it for himself. Yeats suspected that the rooted pre-Christian, indigenous poetic-spiritual reconnection he craved could be deeply unwelcome in Ireland. In fact, in dark moments, he sometimes feared that reconnection to the sacred spaces of a pre-Christian Ireland could endanger life: "Forty years ago my closest friend planned a walk through Ireland … that he might preach the return of those ancient gods that seemed a part of the soil and the blood". Though his poet's soul admired his friend's plan, Yeats recalls "Fearing for his life [because] Irish Christianity is not gentle". So he persuaded the friend to abandon the project.

Later, Yeats regretted this, and recognised with sadness that the kind of Christianity which feared ancient beliefs had "robbed all countries; men once thought their own neighbourhood holy, but now had to discover their Holy Land in an atlas".

A Poet's Tears   *Uma*

Tracing Yeats's tears has helped me to put into words my own lived experience of this "something ancestral in ourselves", this meeting of Celtic spiritual wisdom in Indian philosophy and poetry, that was so vividly intuited by Yeats. In his tears for Tagore, and in his passion for Thoreau, the **Yoga Sutra** *and the* **Upanishads**, *I find a stream that makes sense of my own symbolic collisions: a cycle of stories and songs that spans three decades of living the harmonic resonances between my love for the Fertile Rock of the Burren in the West of Ireland and my passion for a yoga practice, whose home for me was, for many years, in the tribal lands of the Santhali (Dravidian) people in the North of India.*

I've been searching by this writing, looking back over thirty years, to understand why Yeats wept; and that understanding now inspires me to articulate the urgent, deep need for the emergence of the Celtic School of Yoga from its own lost lineage. This understanding now inspires me to reclaim my place in a vast underground network of poets, tantrikas, yoginis *and radical philosophers whose twin inspirations were reverence for the Earth and a love for yoga philosophy as a code for living. Tracing the poet's tears has brought me home to the Celtic heart of my own rooted and enraptured yoga practice.*

Winter Solstice

Jack

While working on the design of the exhibition at Newgrange, I had the opportunity to be in the chamber on December 21st. Watching the assembled dignitaries—prime ministers, presidents and other celebrities—it struck me that, while they were all marvelling at the previously pitch-black chamber lighting up with the mid-winter sun, the real action was going on behind their backs as the souls of the ancestors left the chamber to help, with their wisdom and presence, to propagate the brand new year and keep the seasons turning. Later I wrote and recorded a song about the experience:

Newgrange Bhajan
Beneath the stones, the waiting princes sleep
Bones burnt black and trampled into dust
Enchanted spirals, forgotten secrets keep,
We search for meaning, they won't betray their trust

There was a time when golden hair was long
And fixed to gentle heads with antler pins
There was a time when golden men were strong
And priests were more than punishment for sins
Jaya Bhagavan

Now invited watchers crowd the floor
To follow beams of light like golden string
Hoping that the sun will rise once more
While angels in their stone choir stalls sing

We watch the light till tears come to our eyes
We hold our breath and let our fevers run
But behind our backs, the souls of princes rise
To make love lightly, with a virgin Sun.
Jaya Bhagavan

Triskele and Chamber at Newgrange

4 Music and Poetry

The poet Robert Graves maintained that all true poetry was a prayer to the White Goddess; the goddess of the Earth. In Irish tradition, Bardic poets and musicians were as powerful, if not more so, than kings. This derived to a certain extent from Druidic traditions and survives today in the status and value of the Arts in Irish culture. The power of the poets, their *Shakti*, came from the stories, poems and songs they had learnt and written.

In our yoga practice we use language consciously as a means to rediscover the sacred. We often think of Druids as people with long white robes and magic wands. But in Ireland it was said that the druids dressed normally and that their "wand" was their ability to use words and music to enchant their listeners into new states of mind and heart, and even to sing places and physical objects into being.

Celtic Christian Ireland was divided into 185 *tuatha* (small kingdoms) each with its own king and resident scholar and poet. There were no major concentrations of power, and few people lived in villages or towns as we would understand them today. The poet was often just as important as the king and their magic lay in their voices and poetry. A poem is a physical event which can stretch your mind and body just like a yoga pose. And like a yoga pose, it needs you to stay with it, even with a lack of comfort or understanding, so that you can open up to its meaning. It can stretch you into a new shape.

The power of music is clear in the *Song of Aimhirghin* when Aimhirghin and his people are bargaining with the Tuatha Dé Dannan about the land of Ireland. While at Tara, he makes a judgement that the sons of Mil should retreat nine waves back to sea and approach again. The Dannan summon a storm but Aimhirghin calms the sea by chanting from his heart. In Celtic Yoga we use words, music and myths as instruments to transform our physical practice into a tangible connection with ourselves, with others and with the Earth herself.

Certain forms of music, like beautiful fragrances, awaken associations in us that are primordial, eternal, and ultimate. They call us to the core of our spiritual being. The Sufis say that some music grants us a faint experience of God. Experiments in the physics of acoustics have demonstrated that sound affects reality by actually creating structure. Using radio telescopes, astronomers have found sound throughout every corner of the universe. They have also discovered that some of the haunting sounds that inspire our most sacred traditions are actually cosmic sonic elements, the sounds of the universe itself. This astounding discovery suggests how intimately we are connected with the cosmic matrix, and how deeply it affects us all. It is also clear from consciousness studies that music, chant and sound have direct and dramatic effects on consciousness.

Wayne Teasdale

Ganesh playing the Uileann Pipes, Co Wicklow

These stories, songs and myths are the common dreams of our society and we need them. They function amongst us in the same way that our personal dreams function in our sleep—they help us to communicate with our unconscious minds. But because of this need and for the power they have over us, they have often been appropriated by unaware, and sometimes unscrupulous, religious and political structures, turned into commodities and sold back to us. Today, as many people reject religion, they unknowingly reject the stories and myths, and thereby lose contact with their unconscious minds. One of the functions of Celtic Yoga is to bring these truly magical stories back into our lives through our practice of yoga; our practice of connection.

Music inspires yoga but our practice also inspires our creativity. Our life force flows easier and we come back to our creative spirits in music, poetry, gardening, or wherever our life's purpose takes us. In the Celtic worldview, singing to enchantment needs to have an emotional charge. It needs to be fierce or joyful; happy or sad; contemplative or rowdy. But it can never be insipid, practised for the sake of practice.

It needs passion, passion, passion.

For the druids, the word of truth was paramount. They did not write down their teachings but maintained them orally through the route of repeated recitation... Druidic teaching was originally chanted, just as the Vedas are still chanted by Hindus. This is borne out by the metrical arrangement of texts that were transcribed in the Christian era by stanzas, making recitation easier.

Caitlin Matthews

Disciple:
Can one become a Self-realised being through poetry?
Krishnamurphy:
Depends on the poetry.
Ramana Maharshi assures us that there are four paths to Self-realization.
Firstly, Self-enquiry,
Secondly bhakti – the path of devotion –
Thirdly, service to mankind and,
Fourthly, pursuit of beauty.
Perhaps the true poet can walk all four paths simultaneously.
These will be the poets of the future.

Gabriel Rosenstock, The Pleasantries of Krishnamurphy:

Four Stories

In Irish folklore it is said that if music was played and stories were told the devil could not enter the house.

In Patanjali's Sutras *we are told that the purpose of yoga is to "calm the currents of the mind " (though I prefer to paraphrase Yeats, "to go down to the Hazelwood"). I once heard an aphorism to the effect that in yoga we call this mind in need of calming* Manas, *in Buddhism we call it the Monkey Mind, and in Christianity we call it the Devil. Could it be that living and live stories, poetry and music do calm the mind and the keep the devil out of the house?*

On a CD I made called The Enchanted Island, *I recorded a song which is made up of four stories which were, at least in my mind, related. The song was a chant to the Indian goddess Lakshmi, over which I wove one of Ireland's earliest poems called* The Invocation of Ireland, *but sung to a melody called Port na bPúcaí.*

Here are the stories:
1. The chant which forms the basis for the song is: Om Hrimm Shri Lakshmi Bhyo Namaha. *This is a calling on the goddess to bring abundance and beauty into our lives. The word "Lakshmi Bhyo", which refers to all the forms of Lakshmi, are pronounced very like the Irish Lakshmi Bheo which means the "living Lakshmi".*

2. Thousands of years ago, Ireland was inhabited by a magical race called the Tuatha Dé Danann, the people of the goddess Danu. They were totally at one with the nature of their goddess, the Mother Earth, and as a result had great powers. When the first humans, led by the druid Aimhirghin, were approaching the shores of Ireland, the Danann enveloped the island in an enchanted mist. In order to call the island forth, Aimhirghin composed and sang his invocation. In it he called forth the plains of Tara, and the lakes and rivers and waterfalls of the whole country. It was as if the druid was singing the land into being. As the song reverberated against the shore, the mist cleared and their ship made landfall.

3. After Aimhirghin and his people landed they would eventually come to an agreement that the Tuatha Dé Danann would, from that time on, leave the physical realm and live as the spirits of the land. So they retreated into the lakes, the rainbows, the mountains, the sacred sites, and became known as the "good people" or the Sidhe, or what people today know as the faeries. But these were not the small winged fairies of Victorian literature. These were a race of strong, powerful spirits who happened to inhabit a parallel dimension to that of the physical world as we know it (and, as a woman said to me once, " I don't believe in them—but they are there anyway").

4. The story of the melody completes the picture. Two fishermen, rowing their currach (skin boat) from Dún Chaoin in County Kerry to the Blasket Islands, stopped half way across to listen to music that seemed to be coming from just beneath the surface of the ocean. It was a long, haunting melody which one of the fishermen remembered and later learnt on his violin. He called it Port na bPúcaí, the tune of the faeries. Some people believe, from the sound of the melody, that it was actually the song of a Blue Whale migrating through the Blasket Sound. And whales were mammals who, having emerged from the sea to live on land, decided to go back to the waters in the same way the Tuatha Dé Danann had decided to go back to their places of origin.

Yoga Poetry and Aimhirghin's Song

When I was up in Cae Mabon (a north Wales eco-retreat centre) at Bealtaine *one year, I wrote nine lines of poetry about practising* yoga nidra. *This is what I wrote:*

I am the mud that sticks to the sole.
I am the smell of wild garlic
crushed underfoot.
I am the ocean that soaks the sand.
I am the sweetness of clover honey.
I am the fierce white heat of burning
ash that heats the bones.
I am the pink light of dawn that colours
the hills.
I am the wind that blows rocks
down mountains.
I am the touch of warm hand in hand.
I am the open blanket of heaven, space
between stars.
I am the voice of the wood pigeon in
the trees.

I am the singer of the Mother's songs.
I am the tiny light of hope in the still
darkness of despair.
I am the word-stream that slakes the
teachers' thirst.
I am the bed of the ocean of old
knowings.

I'd organized this poem according to the structure of the philosophy that underpins yoga and tantra, (with each sensory input allied to an element: earth–smell, water–taste, fire–sight, air–touch and space–

hearing), but it felt Celtic to me, because of where it came to me, in a bluebell wood in the mountains of north Wales, at Bealtaine. And I called it Celtic Tantra.

But it wasn't until I shared this poem in a converted cowshed in Clare, at the end of a yoga session I was teaching there, that I could understand enough to hear the Celtic echoes in that poem more clearly. For in that cowshed was a Celtic yogi *called Jack, who knew how to sing Aimhirghin's Song, and when he heard my poem, he was able to show me that my own "Celtic tantra" yoga poetry was an echo of what Yeats called "the one fragment of pagan Irish philosophy come down."*

And my heart sang at the thought of the yoga in Aimhirghin's song, and the Celtic echoes in my yoga poem, and that heartsong brought me straight back to Mr. Yeats, the would-be yogi. *And then I remembered that Yeats had referred so directly to the* Song of Aimhirghin *in his introduction to the translation of the Upanishads that he created with Sri Purohit Swami at the end of his life. And then I knew that if Yeats had had the words for it, he would have recognised himself as a yogi too, just like his childhood hero Henry David Thoreau, a self identified* yogi.

Uma

Practice

Little Breath Songs

The sound of the natural breath is a song. We can hear this song, and we can float mantra—sacred sounds—on the flow of the breath. Some mantras are in the sound of the breath itself.

⚠ *Allow your breath to be effortless and easy, coming and going through the nose at whatever pace naturally arises right now. Listen to the sound of this naturally arising breath and hear its sound, like waves in the tides.*

⚠ *Invite the mantra* so-ham *to be heard in the tides of breath:* so *on the incoming tide of breath and* ham *on the outgoing tide. This mantra is not spoken, it's what we can hear in the breath.*

⚠ *Allow for the the natural breath to grow more spacious, and hear the short mantra* so-ham *on every cycle of breath, until it feels as if this mantra actually describes the sound of the breath, as if there is no difference between the words of the mantra that float on the tide of the breath, and the breath itself:* so *on the inhale and* ham *on the out breath, with growing pauses after the end of the exhale and after the completion of the inhale.*

⚠ *As the breath becomes longer and more free, let go of the mantra* so-ham *and return simply to hearing the sound of the tides of the breath coming and going.*

⚠ *Then, in time with the rhythm of the naturally arising breath, invite other, longer mantras to float singing on the breath.*

⚠ *Hear the mantra* Om Namaha Shivaya *(which can be translated as "With great respect and love, I honour my heart, my inner teacher"), on the incoming tide of breath.*

⚠ *Hear the mantra* Om Parashaktyai Namaha *(which can be translated as "I honour the supreme power of life herself"), on the exhale.*

⚠ *Invite these two long mantras to form a perfectly balanced pair arising together over and over again in every cycle of breath.*

⚠ *Allow* Om Namaha Shivaya *to be an expression of the masculine consciousness of pure being, hear this mantra floating on the inhale.*

⚠ *Allow* Om Parashaktyai Namaha *to be an expression of the feminine energies of life herself, hear this mantra floating on the exhale.*

⚠ *Feel in the mantras on the breath, a sense of the ascent of consciousness on the inhalation and a descent of grace on the exhalation:* Shiva *(pure consciousness) is riding in on the inhale, and* Shakti *(pure energy) is flooding through us on the exhale.*

⚠ *Continue with this conscious awareness of the mantras on the breath for as long as feels comfortable, and then let go of all effort.*

⚠ *Simply listen to the sound of the tides of the effortless breath, hearing perhaps now and then, over these tides of breath, the echoes of the mantras naturally arising or fading away, like the sound of the birds singing over the sea.*

Honouring the Deep Feminine

Before farming, before surplus and greed, before war, there was the Goddess. The land of Ireland herself was seen as her body—her breasts in Kerry, her navel at Uisneach, her *yoni* at Cruachan (Rathcroghan), aligned towards the sun. This reminds us of the *Shakti Pitha* in India, places venerated as sites where parts of body of the goddess Sati fell to Earth.

This Earth, this body of the Goddess, moves around the Sun, creating the dance between the male and female principle. In India this sacred dance is known as the *Tandava*, the dance of bliss; and it is also expressed in the great stone monuments of Ireland.

Newgrange was a cathedral in the form of the passage and womb of the Earth herself, to be visited by the sunlight of the winter solstice, beginning life and the New Year again and again. This was where the god of Love, Music and Poetry, who is the Irish Krishna, was born. His mother was the river Boyne (BoVinda), his father, the Daghda, the king of the gods, representing the sun. Perhaps the greatest hero of Irish mythology was Cúchulainn. His mother was Dechtire which means Good Earth, his father was Lugh, God of Light—his mother was the Earth, his father the Sun.

Sometime around the shift from the Mesolithic to the Neolithic periods, Ireland lost touch with her great goddess and the priests of the new religions tried to extinguish all memory of her devotion. Thousands of years later there was an echo of this shift when the faith changed a second time from Celtic beliefs—which were themselves deeply entangled with older Irish myths—to those of early Celtic Christianity, which even themselves were rooted in older faiths.

When Ireland lost touch with her great goddess, the priests of the new religions tried to extinguish all memory of her devotion. The snakes that Patrick supposedly banished were symbols of her. But she survived, like her children, the Tuatha Dé Danann, because people realised that they could not live without her. So people put her underground in the same way that the Greek Apollo installed the female oracle of Delphi under his

Women in early Ireland travelled an ominous path; once revered symbols of creativity, they became signs of danger and pollution; transformed into virgins, they now needed to be "protected". The church may well have begun by protecting women from the power of the male warriors, but who would now protect women from the power of the male church?

Mary Condren

The Goddess was not a Goddess of power, or power over, but was vulnerable, dependent upon the common humanity of her people to sustain her being. She inspired reverence, not worship; co-operation, not dominance; and she called for an ethics of care and responsibility, for herself and for the Earth.

Mary Condren

Sláinte na bhfear agus go maire na mná go deo—health to the men and may the women live for ever.

Irish toast

Evidence for a sacred marriage with a goddess whose name and association with a sacramental drink has Indo-European roots.

John Waddell

Paps of Anú, Co Kerry

great temple. The poet and mythologist, Robert Graves, believed that there were also such women oracles at Newgrange and that the Druids came to them for advice on any important issue. The great Goddess survived as the sovereignty goddess from whom all Irish kings had to get permission to rule the land. Kingship was male but sovereignty was female and any king had to pay continued reverence to her.

The land was female and it was she who chose who should be king. She often appeared as a hideous creature who offered herself to the prospective king, but when he kissed her or made love to her, she turned into a beautiful woman. She went by several names such as Eirú, Banba and Fodhla, all of whom gave their name to the land of Ireland. Aimhirghin himself was selected by Éiru, who prophesied that his people, the sons of Mil, would rule Ireland.

In Celtic Yoga, dancing with the goddess, rediscovering her sovereignty and re-establishing the balance between her and the male solar principle is at the heart of a practice that honours the deep feminine.

These are not just ancient stories. They are expressions of our own personal and collective dreams which help us to feel the rhythm of the dance between the solar masculine and the deep feminine.

This is the pulse of our lives.

Danu, or Diti, the Great Goddess of the non-Aryan Dravids was the Cow Goddess of India. She was undoubtedly related to the European Goddess Danu... the Goddess of the Irish Tuatha Dé Danaan. In Indian mythology she was murdered by the god Indra, who was the god of the invaders. Danu and her son, Vrta are first described as serpent demons...

Monica Sjöö and Barbara Mor

Whosoever has seen the feet of a woman, let him worship them as those of his guru.

Kubjika Tantra

The sovereignty figure was also the female personification of the land and this is a reminder that landscape features might be experienced as animate entities influencing cultural practice and beliefs. If she was ever venerated, she may have been the object of votive offerings.

John Waddell

All oracles were originally delivered by the Earth-goddess, whose authority was so great that patriarchal invaders made a practice of seizing her shrines and either appointing priests or retaining the priestesses in their own service.

Robert Graves

What is the Deep Feminine?

When we write of the deep feminine, or of women "being the Earth", and when we describe the deep feminine as the Earth herself, we are aware that we may be accused of being old-fashioned and simplistic. But this misses the subtlety and depth of what we understand by the deep feminine.

By linking women to the earth, we do not of course limit women only to their reproductive capacities. On the contrary, we celebrate the extraordinary powers of women in every dimension of life. When we write of the need to recognise the presence of the deep feminine we do so because we seek a genuine re-balancing between masculine and feminine. This requires us to honour the presence within us of the force of life herself, and to heighten awareness of that vital and creative power as the deep feminine.

For complex historical and political reasons, we currently live within a coercive, global hierarchy (*Kyriarchy*—see below for definition) that limits and hurts everyone—men and boys, women and girls—by denying each one of us the full spectrum and depth of our humanity. Our intention in honouring the deep feminine within the Celtic School of Yoga is to free us all from this hurt, and to empower us to rediscover what it is to be fully human once again. To be fully human, to be fully alive and joyous, depends upon healthy respect for both masculine and feminine.

Kyriarchy

Kyriarchy means a complex system of multiple intersecting oppressions. It is derived from Greek words for "master" (*kyrios*) and "dominate" (*arkhein*). This neologism was coined by Elisabeth Schussler Fiorenza, a Romanian feminist theologian and Harvard professor of Divinity. *Kyriarchy* is a useful alternative to the term "patriarchy" which is limited and very often misunderstood. Both these words describe social structures based on elitism, and patriarchal societies can also be sectarian, imperialist and colonial. Gender hierarchy is only one amongst many sources of social disparity.

The Serpent

"Wisdom and immortality would now come, not from observing the rhythms of the seasons and the beauty of nature…Those religions that honoured the Serpent, representing cyclical regeneration and polytheistic philosophies, had to be overthrown. What better way to do it than by making the Serpent the symbol of evil and, thereby, responsible for those disasters which humankind, even with the wildest imagination, could hardly be held liable?

In a society where male bonding and male reproductive consciousness were the operative political philosophies… Female symbolism (such as the serpent) would have to be eradicated entirely from such crucial arenas of power. Christianity would have to have a much firmer grip on the central symbolism of the social structure and, more importantly, whatever ritual the kin would undergo in the future would be formed by the logic of the Father God, rather than the Mother Goddess—an entirely different form of logic…"
Mary Condren

The female principle manifests itself in many cultures in the form of a serpent or a dragon. One of the earliest references is from the Sumerians who lived around modern day southern Iraq about 5,000 years ago. They referred to the Tree of Life, the Tree of Knowledge, and the serpent who guarded both trees. The image of the serpent also adorned the goddesses of Egypt and many other early cultures. It is thought that this was the case because snakes shed their skin and so regenerated themselves in the same way that women regenerate humanity. The serpent was the image of life, rebirth and renewal. Every mythology had some form of World Serpent and she was a basic Indo-European religious symbol. In India, *Kundalini*, the feminine power which is said to rest in the pelvis of every human, is represented as a coiled snake.

The defeat of such a creature represented the defeat of the Goddess faith by a patriarchal, power-based religion. St. George in England, Krishna in India, and Apollo in Greece all killed a serpent to consolidate their own power. And, of course, the representation of the serpent in the Book of Genesis as an evil influence on a woman is possibly the best known of all. Only by killing the serpent, and severing the natural cycle of life and death, could a dualistic, patriarchal culture come into real power.

Though the old beliefs were almost eradicated, the victors in some way recognised that the real power of the Earth belonged to the Goddess. Representations of Patanjali, who is the author of the first written text on yoga, show him with a human torso and a snake's tail, possibly indicating that the roots of yoga, its tail, lie in an earlier goddess based culture.

In the same way, Apollo, having defeated the old goddess faith, kept a woman oracle in a cavern below his temple at Delphi where all the powerful men in Greece went to get advice before any important decision, as if they knew that the feminine intuitive was all-knowing, but at the same time a threat to their own power base. Patrick, who introduced Christianity to Ireland, "banished" snakes from the island, but in the subconscious of the people they remained at the bottoms of holy wells all across the country—eels, salmon and silver serpents.

Scallop Shells *Jack*

As a student archaeologist, I spent some very happy times working on excavations in Dublin and was continually surprised by the large number of scallop shells amongst the debris of the mediaeval city. Most, of course, would have been used as food; but some might well have been part of the cult of St. James of Compostela, whose symbol is the scallop shell. These are worn, even today, by pilgrims on the Camino de Santiago de Compostela in northern Spain.

Robert Graves, in his Greek Myths, *says "Compostela on the northwestern corner of Spain was one of the most popular pilgrimage centres of pre-Christian times…it was formerly named Brigantium" which was dedicated to the Celtic triple goddess Brighid. He maintained that the goddess's symbol, a* kteis *or vulva, in the form of a scallop shell, was adopted by the cult of the new saint James.*

St James's Gate, near where I was working and one of the now demolished portals to the city, was so-called because it was the departure point for large numbers of pilgrims heading for the Camino. The area is still known by that name today. In a convoluted way, the scallop shells I was finding on the mediaeval excavations were another symbol of the triple goddess herself.

Practice

Bringing Love to the Source Within

This simple meditative gesture offers love down into the source of creative power, the deep feminine, and then invites that creative power to rise up and nourish the heart's capacity to love.

When the link between heart energy and pelvic energy is broken we become disconnected from our source power, the deep feminine of our Earth. Lacking this connection we can become depleted, and feel the need to look to others for guidance and instruction. When this connection is restored, and love flows freely down into the source, then vital energy is nourished and we are re-connected to our intuitive wisdom, the deep feminine within each of us.

⚜ *Sit, stand or lie down comfortably, and bring your hands together to the level of your heart with the fingertips touching and thumbs resting against the breastbone.*

⚜ *Exhale and slide hands down, in* yoni mudra *(downward pointing triangle), to the pubic bone, with the index fingertips touching, the thumb tips touching and the palms on the front of the body.*

⚜ *Inhale and return hands to heart, bringing the fingertips to touch again.*

⚜ *Repeat; synchronising breath and movement with awareness.*

In Celtic Irish tradition there is an emphasis on the physical nature of human love and little sense of spiritual transgression in erotic encounters where the greatest sin is to abandon a loved one. In the older sagas women frequently take the initiative in prosecuting affairs of the heart. In stories such as that of Deirdre and Naoise, or Diarmaid and Gráinne, unsanctioned love affairs prompted by the erotic ambitions of a disruptive woman appear to cause chaos and disharmony in the heroic world. Such disorder, however, is more likely the result of a male infringement against the sacred equilibrium between the sexes.

Louis de Paor

A hundred men think I am theirs when I drink wine.
But they go away when I start to think on your talk and mine.
Slieve O'Flynn is quiet, silent with snowdrift's hush,
And my love is like sloe-blossom on the blackthorn bush.

The Blackthorn Bush, anon. 17th century, translated by James Carney.

Celtic Yoginis

Since I was four years old, I have loved yoga, and my delight in practice still retains the joy of the little girl who discovered this great treasure by accident. For the past twenty years, my life has been in service of women, sharing a feminine approach to yoga to support female wellbeing. Physically and psychically, the yoga I practice and teach has always been intuitively, deeply rooted in a Celtic sense of reverence for Mother Earth. But for many years, the names, and goddess forms of feminine power that I have used to describe this yoga have all been Indian.

In India I found an unbroken tradition of devotion to Devi, the goddess. I saw the major deities always with their shaktis, or female sources of power. I discovered the ten great wisdom goddesses, the Dasa Mahavidyas (manifestations of knowledge in goddess form) and the sixty-four yoginis. A yogini can be understood simply as a woman who practises yoga. But yoginis can also be fearsome, supernatural creatures with awesome powers, who need to be worshipped, for fear that they might curse villages, steal babies or suck men dry of semen in the night.

Uma

Since 1997 I have been living and working with the presence of wisdom goddesses and yoginis. And between 2006 and 2014, I was up to my eyes in these expressions of the deep feminine as I wrote a very big fat red book about them, and their relation to women's lives now. Partway through writing Yoni Shakti *I conceived a desire to return to India and lead pilgrimages to the yogini temples, to honour the deep feminine. But a wise Irish colleague of mine took me to task: "Uma," she said, "what are you thinking of? Save your airfares. Come back to Ireland. We have all the goddesses you need right here in your homeland."*

When I looked West I saw that she was right. To rediscover Danu and Brighid, to reconnect with the stories of Macha and the Morrigan, was to recognise these expressions of the deep feminine as Celtic yoginis and wisdom goddesses. This recognition brought me back home into the land of my matrilineal ancestors. As an Irish-English yogini who has birthed three Indian-Irish children, I felt a sense of belonging both to India and to Ireland, but the re-connection to the Celtic yoginis and old Irish feminine archetypes fed my soul and nourished the roots of my yoga practice.

Romano British triple goddess, Corinium Museum Cirencester

Singing into Being

Writing about Christianity in The Second Sex, *Simone de Beauvoir says:*

> For the first time in human history, the mother kneels before her son; she freely accepts her inferiority. This is the supreme masculine victory…

But growing up in Dublin I was told as a small child that, if I wanted something from God, all I had to do was to pray to Mary and she would intercede for me— even if God himself would not have given it to me— because the people of Ireland had a special place in the Virgin's heart. It struck me even then that, if this was the case, she was actually more powerful than God.

Many years later, on a Summer trip to Donegal with my lovely new girlfriend, I saw what appeared to be a string of jewels made from hay that had been put out to dry in clumps on the stone walls. Later the Moon created a huge silver street on the beach at Gaoth Dobhair. The place-names of Donegal were haunting. The English language place-names which were made up by 19th century British army mapmakers, and which are still used today in Ireland, mean little to anyone. But in the original Irish they were poems which sang the landscape into existence.

I realised that the world I was looking at was the song of the Goddess of Sovereignty who was the Earth herself and that the Irish place-names, even in translation, were resonances of that creation. My song, Silver Streets, which is mostly made from these ancient, iconic place-names, was born of that realisation.

Silver Streets

Jack

She walks on the Silver Streets of the night
She walks on the sea
She walks in the Jewelled Fields of the day
She walks with me

She sings with the deer in the Mountains of Snow
She sings with the trees
She sings with the foxes in the Glen of Thorns
She sings with me

She's with us all the way home
She's with us all the way home
She's with us all the way home
To the places she named when the world was born

She swims with the salmon in the Lake of Stones
She swims with the seals
She swims with the shoals in the Bay of Sands
She swims with me

She runs with the hares in the Shaking Bog
She runs with The Reeds
She runs with the stallions in the Hills of the Foals
She runs with me

She's with us all the way home from the Valley of Ghosts
To the Islands of Bones
She's with us all the way home
We only have to cross these Stepping Stones.

She flies with the eagles in the Cliffs of the Wind
She flies with the bees
She flies with the sparrows in the Speckled Hills
She flies with me

She's with us all the way home
She's with us all the way home
She's with us all the way home
To the places she named when the world was born.

Errigal Mountain, Co. Donegal

6 Mythology

Joseph Campbell defined Myth as "other people's religion"; he defined religion as "misunderstood myth". Myths are not stories of actual events in the past, they may be synchronous or even based on such stories, but they do not speak to us with anything approaching historical accuracy. In essence, they are dreams; the dreams of a community and sometimes the dreams of the whole world.

In a manner of speaking these dreams are not true, but at the same time they present the greatest truths we can possibly encounter. In the way that we need our personal dreams to communicate with our sub-conscious minds, we also need our myths to communicate with the true essence of why we are living on this planet, to establish in our hearts the connection that we have with the Earth, the Sun and the other beings who live here. Eventually we gave our myths to priests and bishops and our sexuality to tabloid editors. Then they sold them back to us.

The greatest teaching is **Love this Life.** And our communal dreams—the stories that define us as a people—are a means to loving life. The stories are told to remind us of who we are, to inspire our practice and our lives.

The Celtic spiritual gift is to embody fully the spirit of life. It is a generous and extravagant hospitality, like an opening of the palace of the body to be inhabited by what arises and filled with the music of what happens. Being the songs we hear, being the birds and being the trees and letting sensory awareness directly awaken the whole of life within the body, we are filled with a pure rapture of living. The purpose of this school of yoga is to enable us to hear the music of what happens and let it fill us so completely that we embody the spirit of the living earth and all her creatures.

Once, as they rested on a chase, a debate arose among the Fianna as to what was the finest music in the world.

"Tell us that" said Fionn turning to Oisín.

"The cuckoo calling from the tree that is highest in the hedge" cried his merry son.

"A good sound" said Fionn. "And you, Oscar" he said "what is to your mind the finest of music?"

"The top of music is the ring of a spear on a shield", he cried.

"It is a good sound" said Fionn.

And the other champions told their delight: the belling of a stag across the water, the baying of a tuneful pack heard in the distance, the song of a lark, the laugh of a gleeful girl, or the whisper of a moved one.

"They are good sounds all" said Fionn.

"Tell us Chief", one ventured, "what do you think?"

"The music of what happens" said great Fionn, "that is the finest music in the world."

James Stephens

Cáer, Uma-Parvati and Voices of the Holy Well

I am winding together here threads of three stories of mythical women with Irish and Indian roots. Enchanted by these mythical females, my Indo-Celtic yogini heart has been nourished by the Indian stories of the many forms of the Mother, and by the powerful women, fierce goddesses, and magical girls in the myths of Ireland.

Because the Irish stories were recorded by Christian monks who had their own judgments about women, and because the Indian stories have been shaped by conservative Brahmin views of female conduct, I have always sensed that the truly wild, creative and deep feminine nature of these powerful females could not be heard clearly.

In my teaching about yoga tantra *for women's vitality and empowerment, I listen carefully to the voices of girls and women, winding together all the lost threads, to heal and mend broken spirits and tired bodies. There are three stories that are especially intertwined for me:*

Cáer Ibormeith is the lost love of wandering Aengus, god of love and poetry; Uma-Parvati is the consort of Shiva, lord of yoga and dance; and the Well Maidens are the women who care for the source of life at the Holy Wells, nourishing travellers and ensuring that the voices of the wells are heard clear and true.

One summer's day in the Burren, a wise healer friend told me the tale of the Rape of the Well Maidens, from the French Romance of the Conte de Graal, based on Celtic stories. Through the abuse of the beautiful women who cared for the wells, the voices of the waters were silenced, the springs dried up, and all growth ceased. People had entered a time of suffering, pain and searching for beauty and abundance that was lost when balance and trust between masculine and feminine was broken.

The very next dawn, bathing in a Holy Well, I heard an echo of this haunting story in the clear song of the spring-water. It brought together in a single, healing stream, all the myths of the goddesses, from India and Ireland. The bed over which the stream ran reminded me of yogini *Angela Farmer's story of how Uma-Parvati discovered the fluid, vital flow of movements that inspired Shiva to give yoga to the world. It was Parvati's sensual joy, as she bathed each morning, that was the source of yoga.*

And over the bed of that recovered myth, ran my delight in the voice Yeats created for wandering Aengus, finding his glimmering girl by the hazel wood stream. Aengus's voice was clear and strong, but until that dawn moment bathing in the Holy Well, I had never been able to hear Cáer's own voice. I had often wondered what she might have said to Aengus when he found her... and why she appeared to him in his dreams in the first place.

I began to feel that maybe, in her human form, in the days when she was not a great white swan, Aengus's lost love could have been called to the wellsprings of the West of Ireland to hear the songs of the ghosts of the well maidens who had been so abused. And perhaps one of the reasons Cáer appeared to Aengus in his dreams was to ask him to join her, so that together they could sing the healing songs and poems that would free the ghosts of the well maidens from their pain.

Practice

Dream Yoga

Yoga can help us to recognise and navigate those states of consciousness in which we experience dreams, or insights and inspirations.

Here is a simple practice that can cultivate our capacity to recall dreams and welcome creativity. It helps us to grasp the tails of those precious creatures, the lost dreams and insights, that often disappear into the depths of the forest of forgetfulness, when we wake up in the morning.

- *Before you go to sleep at night, rest, conscious and aware of the process of settling.*

- *Use some of the techniques of* yoga nidra, *for example, watching your easy natural breath coming and going, feeling your physical body, heavy in your bed, moving your awareness around the body as you rest.*

- *Let go of the conscious practice of awareness.*

- *Hover in the place between being asleep and being awake.*

- *Notice what it is like to be here.*

- *If there is a dream you would like to recall, or a creative process in which you are involved, hold in your heart all that is most vivid to you about your dream or your creative project. Let your heart be a nest, to hold the egg of your dream safely as you fall asleep.*

- *When you wake up in the morning, before doing anything else at all, allow yourself to hover in the space between being asleep and being awake. If necessary, set an alarm for half an hour earlier than you actually need to get up, so you can rest consciously in the space between sleeping and waking.*

- *In this place, before you move, return to the practices of* yoga nidra, *noticing your breath moving and your body resting.*

- *Move your conscious attention around the body and then invite that awareness into your heart, and listen to the song of the bird in the nest of your heart. What you hear will be what you need to pay attention to right now.*

Colman's Well, the Burren, Co. Clare

The Fall

Jack

I have often wondered if the Garden of Eden was not in Mesopotamia—the land between two rivers in present day Iraq—where civilisation is said to have been born.

Before the advent of farming, people lived as hunter-gatherers and cherished the Earth as their mother who, though sometimes cruel, was always fair and loved them back. The mythologist Joseph Campbell believed that all pre-farming cultures had a goddess faith. It was not until farming ushered in surplus and trade, which in turn sparked envy and greed, that there was a need for male gods of war.

Archaeologists speak of a "weapons horizon", a time when the numbers of weapons found in their excavations suddenly increased. It happened exactly at the point of the development of farming—with the knowledge of domestication of animals and plants came weapons, power over others, and the strange idea of land ownership.

To gain and keep their new power, and to ensure that new young soldiers were ready to fight and die for the elite aristocracy (who were, of course, the biggest, most ruthless thugs around), war-based religions were developed to supplant the old faiths. And with a masterful stroke, the image of the snake—which had once represented the renewal of life and the goddess—was manipulated so that she and woman were blamed for the very act that deposed her.

And we lost the garden.

Some popular books might portray the shift from a Mesolithic economy (desperate foragers wandering in search of food) to a Neolithic economy (farmers living off the fat of the land) but ethnographic data often reveals the opposite (hunter gatherers moving contentedly through a cycle of seasonal changes and rejecting the drudge of agricultural labour undertaken by their farming neighbours)…

The Neolithic is characterised by an increase in warfare and there is clear evidence of this in the Early Neolithic of Britain. This involves attacks on sites, arrows embedded in skeletons and a recent study of 350 British Neolithic skulls in which about one in 20 gave evidence of trauma. Many of the Irish Neolithic houses show signs of destruction by fire. But the violence does not seem to involve the Mesolithic population because they are all Neolithic arrowheads and there is no evidence for Mesolithic weapons…

There is also an increase in meat in the diet and a decrease in fish.

JP Mallory

The Dance of the Sun, Moon and Earth—The Celtic Year

Anything powerful moves in cycles and waves, integrating times of rest and lull with times of activity and receptivity. For example, the creative process, the tides of the sea, the phases of the moon, the menstrual and circadian (daily) cycles, and experiences of sexual arousal, response and rest, are all dances of our lives with the world. A Celtic approach to yoga honours and nourishes these cycles, and empowers us to dance to this rhythm of power with joy, and to recognise that the need to rest is part of the dance.

Retreats and training courses are guided by the intelligence of the land and light, and the lunar and solar patterns throughout the year. The principal activities in the school honour significant times in an extended Celtic calendar:

Imbolg (February 1st)—celebrating the White Goddess as Brighid, the goddess of fertility who poured the future into the Shannon River from her great Iron cauldron.

Spring Equinox (March 21st)—We don't seem to have any record of an older festival but today the festival of the Spring equinox could be said to be celebrated on St Patrick's Day (March 17th).

Bealtaine (May 1st)—celebrating Danu (of Ireland, Greece and India) and her three daughters who constitute the physical land of Ireland, at the site of the Omphalos (the navel of the world) at Uisneach. Close by was a fire from which all fires in Ireland were lit.

Summer Solstice (June 21st)—Midsummer. In the West of Ireland this is usually celebrated on June 23rd with bonfires, music and dancing as St John's Eve.

Lughnasa (August 1st)—celebrating Lugh, god of light. This was the festival of the harvest, which included climbing hills and swimming in lakes.

Autumn Equinox (September 21st)—celebrating the feast of Mabon, the continental avatar of Aonghus. This was also called Michaelmas, the feast of the Archangel Michael, who was the one to drive Adam and Eve and the snake out of the Garden of Eden.

Samhain (October 31st; Halloween)—celebrating the *Cailleach* (Kali) or Morrigan the witch goddess.

Winter Solstice (December 21st)—celebrating Aonghus, son of youth and god of love and birth.

Every secret of art, every subtlety of knowledge, and every diligence of healing that exists, from the Tuatha Dé Danann had their origin. And although the Faith (Christian) came, these arts were not driven out for they are good.

RAS Macallister

The archetype is an archetype because it represents a past reality; its power over us as an internal image is so profound because it was once an experienced fact of the external world. Our history as a species is stored in our genes; and no matter how hard patriarchy tries to suppress our past matriarchal history, it keeps "bobbing to the surface" —in worldwide archaeological ruins, icon, and myths, as in our dreams.

Monica Sjöö and Barbara Mor

A myth is an anonymous, traditional story concerned with deities, heroes or ancestors who embody dimly perceived truths whose roots are in our innermost being.

James MacKillop

Bealtaine Festival at Uisneach, Co Westmeath

Samhain (October 31st)

Uma

At this time for many years I have held yoga retreats in Italy or in Ireland. The spirit of Kali in the time of Samhain was celebrated in yogic fashion by marking the beginning of the retreat with a ceremonial burning of old burdens, to free our souls as we entered into the New Year. Whatever you wished to be free from could be written down on a piece of paper and burned in the fire. And then, before sleeping, the group would get ready for bed and lie down together in the dark, snuggled up warm and cosy under blankets. Lit only by the flames from the fire that had burnt our burdens, we would enter into a yoga nidra practice. In that liminal space of awareness, at the limits of the old year, we would invite the intuitive wisdom of the heart, lightened of its burdens by the earlier burning, to welcome in new purpose and direction for the coming year. Wordlessly, after the practice had finished, everyone would go off to their beds, to dream into the new year. Mouna *(silence) was kept until after breakfast was finished the next morning, when the breaking of the silence marked the beginning of the New Year. This is a way to honour the time of Samhain with the spirit of Kali.*

Bealtaine (May 1st)

Jack

In the Burren of County Clare on the first day of May 2011, I was wandering and wondering about the feast of Bealtaine, *the Irish name for that most auspicious of days, when the whole of the fertile rock was lit up by a low sun shining under clouds from the western horizon. The light bounced, reflected and refracted between the grey of the limestone and the grey of the clouds until it seemed that I was watching a memory and a hope of summer—a memory of Homer's Island of the Cattle of the Sun, of the birth of the Celtic sun-god Lugh in the shining seas of the the Aegean, and of the nymph Calypso, daughter of Atlas and called Atlanta, who gave her name to the ocean on the whose shores I was standing, and whose island of Ogygia some people believed was Ireland.*

The light brought a hope for the packs of feral goats who roam the uplands; for the lizards who come out only to lie on the heat of a sun-baked rock; and for the rock itself with its fossilised memory of a tropical sea, nine degrees south of the equator, where this strange, magical landscape was born.

Brighid's "Cross", celebrating the Spring in the form of a Swastika *which originally denoted good fortune.*

8 The Yoga of Wandering—the Immram

The ancient Irish manuscripts were all written down by Early Christian monks, wishing to preserve the old tales in their new Christian context. But they were obviously attracted by the world they were describing and seemed to want to voyage into a pure pre-Christian Celtic world.

An *Immram* was a wonder tale where the heroes set out to sea in a small boat and came into contact with the otherworld, with all its gods and timeless dimensions, its ice towers, mountains of fire and strange creatures. Their aim was to discover what they could find for its own sake, just by wandering without eye to profit or conquest. Their navigation was a desire for learning but also, in itself, a form of spiritual enlightenment. Their journey was the destination.

It is this spirit of adventure and curiosity for their own sake that is one of the defining elements of the Celtic and pre-Celtic mind. This wandering is a love of being for its own sake. It is not only the physical travelling, but it is the delight in looking at the world in all her manifestations and not just following the teaching of a single way or a single perspective.

When we set out on an *Immram* we never know what we will encounter. *Lila*, the sanskrit term for the play of the universe, is always around us. We can settle our *karmic* debt (the consequences of our actions) and live our lives according to our *dharma* (our vocation), but because *Lila* is a playful adventure, anything can happen.

To journey on an *Immram* is to seek out other ways of knowing and to be always open to the unexpected. In the Irish tradition, this journeying was seen as an essential way to contact the other world. But that world was beyond the Western Ocean and no sailor knew which direction to travel. So they were prepared to go from adventure to adventure, their course mapped by the Sun, and to be fully engaged with the rapture of the wild Earth as they met her.

… the hero is often on a father quest. This is often associated with a virgin birth and his mother tells him it was the sun or whatever. Then he sets off on a father quest. In Ulysses, it's the reverse. Stephen is in quest of his spiritual father. He knows who his earthly father is but he must find who his spiritual father is. Who is the giver to him of his character? Who is the symbol of that ground or source of his being with which his conscious ego system has to put itself in relation? This spiritual father is not necessarily the same as his physical father.

Declan Kiberd, Ulysses and Us

The wisdom to be gleaned from The Odyssey *is clear enough: that there is nothing better in life than when a man and woman live in harmony and that such happiness, though felt intensely by the couple themselves can never be fully described. It can merely be evoked, either by comparison or by contrast. Homer set out to heroicise the domestic, even as Joyce wishes to domesticate the heroic.*

James Brown, A Companion to James Joyce

In 1976, Tim Severin recreated the 6th century wandering of Brendan the Navigator across the Atlantic Ocean from Kerry to Newfoundland.

In a Celtic approach to yoga, this spirit of adventure and wandering is brought into our daily lives. The prospect of wandering on the wide ocean can be daunting. Wandering inside, exploring the ocean of our feelings and responses in daily life can also evoke fear. Loving the journey is the opposite of fear. There will be fear in our lives but we need to minimise it. Love is to be open; fear is to be closed, and we often live by fear disguised as day–to–day routine. In the same way as we need courage to go out on the ocean, we also need courage to go on with our everyday life.

I went everywhere
With longing in my eyes
Until here
In my own house
I felt truth filling my sight

Lalla

Come away, O human child
To the waters and the wild
With a faery, hand in hand
For the world's more full of
Weeping than you can understand.

WB Yeats

The Celtic otherworld is variously imagined under a hill, where the two worlds collide. Whatever its geographic location, the otherworld is perilously close to the human with fluid boundaries allowing movement either way. Likewise, the dead inhabit a world within reach of the human; women call out a warning before throwing out dirty water at night lest the dead are passing by. A swirling gust of wind is caused by otherworld dwellers moving from one location to another. The landscape itself, gateway to the otherworld, appears uncreated and ever-lasting, an eternal world here and now forever.

Louis de Paor

The Heroine's Journey

Jack

As I was speaking at a workshop about The Odyssey *and the Hero's Journey, a friend asked me what I thought about the Heroine's Journey. She had read a book charting such a journey and positing a parallel story to that of the hero. But to me it seemed that the Heroine's Journey must be different. Whereas the classical hero has to leave his home, go out into the world, survive a series of tests and return home powerfully triumphant, the heroine has to descend into her soul and emerge with a recognition of her own power.*

Thousands of years ago, after the fading of the goddess tradition, the feminine began to be forced into a secondary place in society. The new faiths—which included both women and men—had to keep her underground in order to consolidate their authority. Though her continuing presence was recognised by those who understood the true source of their own power, she had to be hidden and so she became the Oracle at Delphi, living in a cave below the temple; or she became the wise or sensual woman who was feared and persecuted as a witch; or she became the subservient housewife who did as her husband instructed—he himself being, of course, disconnected from his own spiritual life and disempowered by the elite political and religious classes.

The Heroine's Journey is not that of Odysseus sailing to Ithaca plagued by storms, monsters and Penelope's one hundred and eight suitors; it is the journey down into the underworld and back out into the light.

Biking by Mistake into the Burren

Uma

In 1987, I was a twenty-one year old undergraduate cyclist with a passion for old English poetry and a vague but profound reverence for the sacred places of pre-Christian Ireland. It was the summer that Irish cycling hero Sean Kelly was at the top of his game, and it seemed that anyone on a bike, especially a friendly young woman on an insanely over-packed touring machine who had hundreds of miles in her legs, got a hero's welcome.

One bright morning I sped down the hill at the South end of the Burren, where the limestone pavements reach right out into the Atlantic. And I literally fell off my bike. I was shocked, astonished, delighted, amazed, adrift and at home all at the same time. I swore. Then I breathed in the prana- *filled air and asked "What is this place?"*

With the stupidity and trust of youth, I hadn't bothered to find out anything about the land I'd be cycling through: the itinerary had all been about arrivals at destinations to make drawings, and how to find my lover in Galway city. So I'd had no idea at all that I'd find myself cycling through an ancient coral seabed that had once been just south of the equator on the other side of the world. I was clueless. But my heart was stolen forever by the Fertile Rock. Thirty years later I'm still coming back to retrieve the little parts of it that fell down the cracks on that first morning.

9 Pranayama—A Song of Breath

A connection with the sung spirit of the land is crucial to our wellbeing. Our naturally arising breath is the living, breathing song of the earth; and learning to dance with the life force that she brings into our bodies is vital in the truest meaning of the word. This dancing with the song of the breath requires a subtle intimacy. It involves the awareness of courting *prana shakti* (the power of the life force which many cultures see as a form of the goddess). It is a way to enchant her, to sing her and to dance her into being, the way we sing the land and our lives into existence.

Pranayama is often translated as breath control or breath extension, but it can be more fruitfully understood as cultivating an intimacy with breath, as voicing the breath-song or playing with the rhythm and flow of breath, so as more fully to welcome the vital energy carried on each breath.

Through attentive intimacy with our own breath-song we begin to understand that many of the formal *pranayama* methods that are usually taught as techniques to be learnt, do in fact derive from spontaneous breath patterns. For example, many powerful alterations or suspensions of breath-flow naturally occur in those moments of heightened awareness or thresholds in our lives, perhaps when we encounter intense pleasure or pain, fear or joy. By becoming aware of such naturally arising breath patterns, we can harness the effects of the breath in yoga practice and in our everyday life.

One of the remarkable features of Dún Aonghusa is the presence of a chevaux-de-frise outside one of its ramparts. Such bands of upright stones are generally believed to have had a defensive role, retarding the approach of an attacking force. In a major study of this phenomenon, Luis Berrocal-Rangel shows that the stones probably had an equally important symbolic purpose.

He cites the Greek myth of the foundation of Thebes by Cadmus, who, instructed by the oracle at Delphi to found a town, encountered a dragon guarding a spring. When the hero killed the dragon, Athena appeared and told him to sow the dragon's teeth. He did so and a group of fully armed men sprang from the ground. Five of these supernatural Spartoi, the fierce "sown men", helped him found the city. Berrocal-Rangel argues that the clusters of upright stones found at Bronze Age and Iron Age forts in various parts of Europe were not just a hindrance but also had a symbolic protective role.

It is an intriguing thought that the prehistoric significance of Dún Aonghusa was enhanced by the presence of a phalanx of formidable stone warriors.

John Waddell

There are some special places in the world where the very quality of air means that simply breathing is a pranayama in itself. Dún Aonghusa, named after the god of Love, Music and Poetry and perched on a 200 metre high sheer cliff on the island of Inis Mór at the entrance to Galway Bay, is one of these places. We can imagine that it must have been used as a temple to the winds; even to stand there and to breathe with awareness is to be enlivened.

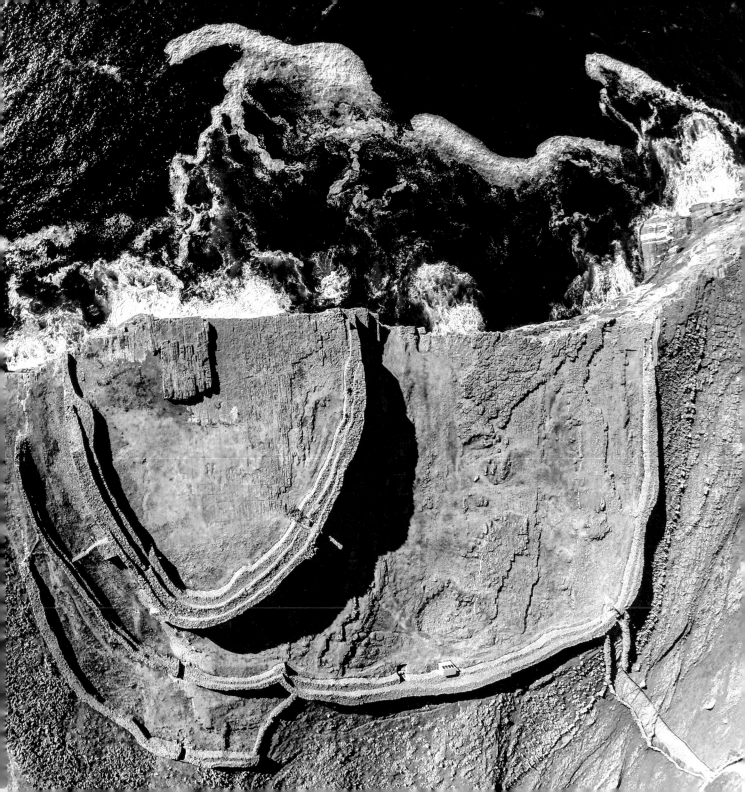

Deep Ecology—the Intimacy of Breathing

Intelligent and sensitive practice of *pranayama* is about receiving and giving. It is an intimate relationship, a deep ecology that teaches us how to sustain and optimize vitality when we need to, and how to share energy generously when we are able. The basis of this ecology is our recognition that the energy or *Prana Shakti* in the breath is not ours: we do not own her, we only invite her to inhabit us for the time we are alive. Through subtle attention to our own breath, we invite *Prana Shakti* into our bodies as an honoured guest. To offer hospitality and intimacy to this source of vitality is to be fully alive.

This aspect of Celtic Yoga practice includes subtle use of psychic awareness to direct a very slow and subtly nourishing audible and feminine "ocean breath" around the network of energy streams. For this to work, the breath needs to become effortlessly slow, otherwise *Prana Shakti* feels rushed and she gets lost, or she misses the stream of breath because it is too quick for her. She doesn't like to be harried. Court her slowly. The slower the breath, the more chance there is that it will charm her to enter your body.

This kind of subtle, slow and very feminine approach to *pranayama* cultivates an exquisite sensitivity of awareness that is deeply hospitable to *Prana Shakti* and her presence within us promotes joy and vitality in every aspect of life, especially in intimacy, as a way to manage pain, or to optimize responsiveness to creative cycles.

With passionate practices
I held the reins secure on my mind and
made the breath one column.
Then the new moon's clear nectar
descending into me,
nothing pouring into Nothing.

Lalla

Day and night, be aware with each breath,
and live there...
Tell me the inner meaning of my two
breathings, the one warm, the other cool.

Lalla

Petra Fertlis, the Fertile Rock,
The Burren, Co Clare

Practice

Breathing your Full Measure into the Earth

⚘ *Whatever position you are in, feel the places where you touch the earth.*

⚘ *Know that these places—perhaps your feet, your back, your belly or your hands—are places to meet with the living presence of the deep feminine.*

⚘ *Feel that these meeting places are tender junctions, holy places where your body feels the earth beneath.*

⚘ *Invite your awareness to be a pilgrim to these holy places.*

⚘ *Welcome these places where you meet the earth.*

⚘ *Feel in these meetings that you and she are the same.*

⚘ *Breathe into her, and welcome her into you.*

⚘ *On the exhale, invite your awareness to travel down through these meeting points, letting the full measure of you be breathed down into the earth.*

⚘ *Breathe out and down, your awareness moving down as deep as you are tall.*

⚘ *Let the end of your exhale be the beginning of your rootedness.*

⚘ *Breathe in and up and out, your awareness moving up as high as you are tall.*

⚘ *Let the end of your inhale be the start of your expansion into the space above your crown.*

⚘ *Breathe the full measure of you down into the earth beneath you.*

⚘ *Breath the full measure of you up into the air above you.*

⚘ *Be breathed by the living earth. Three times or for as long as you would enjoy.*

Practice

Diamond Breathing

The triangle of breath in the nose is a beautiful basic focus for cultivating breath awareness. Feel the different directions from which the flow of breath is drawn in from outside, and notice how the breath expands out in different directions when it leaves. Noticing these flows cultivates a sense of connection between the breath that is inside, and the energy that is outside.

These flows are subtle, and with practice it is possible to direct them through awareness alone, without using fingers to close and open the nostrils. The triangle of breath in the nose can be just a starting point from which to direct energy on the breath through the many other triangles that can be perceived to exist throughout the body. It is possible to breathe awareness through alternate upward and downward pointing triangles (*Shiva* and *Shakti*) to elicit optimal awakening and arousal.

🔺 *Breathe in with the awareness travelling along an upward pointing triangle, from the nostrils to the eyebrow centre.*

🔺 *Exhale down along the nostrils.*

🔺 *Continue to extend awareness of this triangle down to its base behind the breasts on the exhale.*

🔺 *Pause with awareness here to inhale.*

🔺 *Exhale down from behind the breasts, with the breath travelling along a downward pointing triangle whose lower point is in the source place at the base of the pelvis (*yonisthana *or* muladhara*).*

🔺 *On the next inhale, invite breath awareness back up along the sides of this triangle to return to the place behind the breasts.*

🔺 *Exhale with the awareness resting behind the breasts.*

🔺 *Inhale back up along the upward pointing triangle to the eyebrow centre.*

🔺 *By breathing along the joined upward and downward pointing triangles, create a diamond of psychic awareness along which to guide the breath. Continue as long as you like and then, at the end, pause with the attention behind the breasts, and breathe the whole of the awareness into the heart centre.*

Practice

Back-body Triad Breath

This practice is based on what is probably the oldest musical rhythm—the count of one, two, three.

🔱 *Lie comfortably on your back on the floor.*

🔱 *Stretch your hands and fingers, arms straight, fingertips pointing towards the ceiling, palms facing each other.*

🔱 *Move your breath into your back body and feel the space behind your heart press into the softness of your mat.*

🔱 *Try to hear a slow steady rhythm in the natural world. Everything works in rhythms— your heart-beat, the sun rising and setting, the movement of the tides, the sound of the rain. There are millions of different rhythms sounding everywhere at any one time. To make music and dance with our breath, all we have to do is to merge into one of them.*

🔱 *Breathe in for three slow beats; breathe out for three slow beats.*

🔱 *Repeat nine times and then allow your breath to come back to normal.*

🔱 *Allow your arms to float down to the floor and rest with a normal breath.*

Experiential Anatomy—Learning to Know Ourselves

The physical body is our vessel for the journey of life. To live fully we need to know how to care for and maintain her. We need to honour the nature of our own constitution and temperament to support our weaknesses and enhance our strengths. Celtic Yoga recognises that the practices of yoga— conscious movement, breath and stillness—are all tools to enhance our understanding of the nature of our own bodies. It is important when we practise yoga to respect our particular potentials and limits.

The safest and most nourishing way to experience yoga is to allow the practices to grow from a directly embodied knowledge of structural and functional anatomy. Experiential anatomy is the process of learning about the body by exploring her functions and structures through kindness, interest and acute observation. When clarity of understanding and compassion are joined, we experience yoga. The word yoga itself is the same word as the latin *Iugum* and from the Indo-European root *Yugóm* meaning "to join". The name of the jugular vein comes from this word; it joins the heart and the head.

Our bodies are unique creations. A Celtic School of Yoga approach to anatomy is compassionate and intelligent, and promotes vitality and health by honouring plurality and difference at the level of anatomy and physiology.

Recent Western scientific research into the functioning of the human body is beginning to affirm yogic understanding of our physical form as a web of interconnected, rhythmic, communicative impulses. Researches by Dr Daniel Keown, and by Langevin and Schleip explore how the flows of energy that yogis identify as *nadis*, or channels for the vital force of life energy or *prana*, can be mapped in the structure of the myo-fascial meridians, the fluid envelopes that enclose our soft tissues.

Yogic perspectives on the *koshas*, or five different dimensions of being can be understood to resonate with contemporary research into neural

Lines of flow [or meridians] through the structure of the body have been recognised and explored in all Asian cultures… In India the lines of flow are called 'nadis' and the life-energy force, which flows through them, is called 'prana'. These lines of flow… radically affect our health and potential if they are obstructed or depleted. In the West these concepts are new… but with the work of the Yogini Ida Rolf, bodywork practitioners in the West have become more interested in lines of flow and connection through the soft tissue structure of the body… the 'tensegrity' model accounts for the lightness of the skeleton by accounting for the tensile forces of fascial tissues that act like rigging on a sailing ship and support the skeleton, drawing open the joints and freeing them from overly compressive forces that cause undue wear. Fascial tissue is the wrapping layer that surrounds, separates and connects all the individual organs, muscles and other structures of the body. This fascial tissue is a network of tissue that penetrates and supports the whole structure.

Christopher Gladwell

*Spinning body wheels from the 8th Century Irish manuscript, **The Book of Kells***

oscillations, or brain waves. States of mind, and feelings of heart and mood that can be consciously cultivated through yoga practice are being mapped as interconnected experiences by pioneering and popularizing scientists such as Norman Doidge and Dr Bessel van der Kolk.

Since the 1980s, research in the field of psychoendoneuroimmunology (the study of the interaction between psychological processes and the endocrine, nervous and immune systems of the human body), has begun to establish the biological basis of yoga's mind-body physiology.

Discoveries about polyvagal theory, presented by cutting-edge scientists such as Stephen W Porges, can be seen to support the assertions of our yogic texts that we inhabit a living intelligence. Daniel J Siegel's work, and earlier observations made by Candace Pert, show that there is no disconnection between different systems of the body, nor between our inner landscape and our environment. Dr Michael Gershon's research indicates how our gut flora, our enteric brain, our "gut feeling", our immune function, sexual interest, mood and energy levels are all inter-dependent.

Yoga, rooted in subjective experience of the interconnectivity of human bodily systems, is at last starting to acquire some objective scientific explanations for its rationale. These objective researches provide further understanding of how intelligent and compassionate yoga practice can assist us to navigate this beautiful vessel through the whole of our lives with optimal joy and vitality.

We have begun to understand how overwhelming experiences affect our innermost sensations and our relationship to physical reality—the core of who we are. We have learnt that trauma is not just an event that took place some time in the past: it is also the imprint left by that experience on mind, brain, and body. This imprint has on-going consequences for how the human organism manages to survive in the present… the act of telling the story doesn't necessarily alter the automatic physical and hormonal responses of bodies… for real change to take place, the body needs to learn that the danger has passed and to live in the reality of the present. Our search to understand trauma has led us to think differently not only about the structure of mind but also about the processes by which it heals.

Bessel van der Kolk MD

A Burren Limestone in Greece

Jack

I have always felt a very strong attraction to Greece. To me, the land and the sea scintillate with the very essence of what the Tantrics *call* spanda, *the joyful, twinkling rhythms of life. There seems to be some intangible connection between Ireland and Greece which has been mythologised in the belief that the Tuatha Dé Danann came from somewhere on the shores of the Aegean Sea and that Ireland is Ogygia, the island of the magical nymph Calypso where Odysseus spent seven years away from his home at Ithaca.*

I spend as much time there as I can, especially sailing around the Ionian Sea trying to find my own Ithaca. "Ionian" is so called after Io (the Moon) who was the Greek goddess of the White Cow, the same meaning as many places in Ireland called BoVinda, goddess of the white cow, and redolent of one of the the names given to Krishna.

One beautiful island I have been back to many times is Paxos, just south of Corfu. On one recent trip I found another connection to Ireland. Right beside an old pilgrimage place was a piece of limestone pavement almost exactly like that in the Burren where I live.

Songbirds   *Jack*

One of my abiding memories of a deep nourishing retreat in 2015 on the island of Inishboffin (the island of BoVinda) is of a learned friend coming to tell me about new research she had found which showed that if musicians spent a certain amount of time playing or singing, they would turn on a gene in their bodies which was involved in song perception and production in songbirds. Here is part of the abstract of that article from the science journal Nature, *published in March 2015:*

> Here, we investigated the effect of music performance on the genome-wide peripheral blood transcriptome of professional musicians by analyzing the transcriptional responses after a 2-hr concert performance and after a 'music-free' control session. The up-regulated genes were found to affect dopaminergic neurotransmission, motor behavior, neuronal plasticity, and neurocognitive functions including learning and memory. Particularly, candidate genes such as SNCA, FOS and DUSP1 that are involved in song perception and production in songbirds, were identified, suggesting an evolutionary conservation in biological processes related to sound perception/production.

Singing together, like birds in the woods, could bring us into harmony, not just with each other, but with all the singing creatures on the bright Earth.

Learning to Respect our own Rhythms

Uma

I notice that there is a yoga here in simply noticing. The intention of a Celtic yoga practice is to show up, to practise being in a space of awareness, to cultivate, as a natural state of being, always and everywhere noticing what arises; being naked, present and alive to what cycles unfold. This is why it's worth being in the same place at the same time each morning, when we can. We see what stays the same and what changes, both in ourselves, and in our intimate relation to the world we inhabit.

This is why paying attention to menstrual patterns is an important yoga for women, and for the men who live with them. With attention to the physical changes that accompany the turning of these cycles (or their waning as we reach menopause), we can cultivate a self-knowledge also of psychic and emotional shifts. This is an inner yoga that grows from compassionate observance of our body's changes that connects us to the wider cycles of the world's energies. This is a practice of yoga.

As I tracked erratic menstrual cycles early one Spring, I noticed a powerful tide turning in the shift after Imbolg *towards* Bealtaine*: there was a move in me and in the world, from cautious waiting towards joyful arrival.*

This subtlety of observance helps me to notice and respect the emotional and mental ripples caused by shifts in the endocrine system. Learning to read these signs is for me the yoga of swadhyaya. This is usually translated as "self study", and is understood to mean the study of holy scriptures. But swadhyaya *comes alive for me also in the observations I make of the physical body, the vessel that carries me through life. I believe if we pay attention, then a depth of the understanding, and true self-knowledge comes from respecting our own rhythms.*

Milky Way, just before Moonrise,
Connemara, Co Galway

11 Somatic Intelligence—Understanding Rhythms and Cycles

Celtic Yoga empowers us to feel connected and alive, to read the subtle signals of our own bodies, and to welcome these signs as a clear guide to how to live. We need to cultivate an awareness of what our bodies are calling for, so that we don't need to ask teachers or others to tell us what is right for us; we simply know and feel the right thing to do. The practice redresses the imbalance between *Tapas* (endeavour, endurance and discipline) and *Santosa* (acceptance, contentment and happiness).

Our rhythms and cycles include:

Daily cycles of energy and relaxation

Sleep cycles

Digestive rhythms

Menstrual cycles

Breathing cycles

Sexual cycles of arousal and lack of interest

Movements of vital energy such as prana *and* apana

Ageing

Death and transformation

Parenting

Relationship

Cyclical life is a wonderful means of regeneration without which we would run down and die. The rhythmic pattern acts as an inner framework within which we can pace our lives to use our energy more efficiently and wisely, and feel a greater sense of embodiment and stability. The more you are in touch with all the organic rhythms of your body and nature, the more alive you will feel. It is well recognised that cyclical rhythms are vital for the healthy functioning of our bodies and souls. Our beings are incredible orchestrations of activity, responding to both external and internal cues and triggers. The most obvious cycles in our lives are seasonal, *circadian* (day/night rhythm), and *ultradian* (occurring over 90–120 minute cycle) and of course the menstrual cycle.

The observation and respect of all these different cycles and rhythms brings a knowledge of our deeper nature, of who we really are. When we realise that eternity is right here now, that it is within our possibility to experience our own truth, we realise that we were never born and will never die.

γνῶθι σαυτόν—*Know Thyself.*

Written on a stone in the forecourt of the Temple of Apollo and the Oracle's cave at Delphi in Greece.

Exhilaration is the Breeze
That lifts us from the Ground
And leaves in another place
Whose statement is not found.

Returns us not, but after time
We soberly descend
A little newer for the term
Upon Enchanted Ground

Emily Dickinson

In short, youth is a state to be put behind us as we grow taller and deeper and fuller.... The human species, possessed with a brain whose genius is unlimited learning and adaptation, is a species that is genetically designed to age by growing. Not to expect to grow is to misunderstand what it means to be human. Not to do so is to fail in the God-given task of living a fully human life. To expect the opposite is, in effect, to sin against life and its biological promise.

Thomas Hanna

A page from the 7th Century Irish manuscript, ***The Book of Durrow***

Written over the entrance to the cave of the Oracle at Delphi was "Know Thyself". A great part of this knowledge is to realise that we are the total of all the rhythms in our physical, spiritual and communal lives. Our purpose is to dance with these rhythms.

Why the Menstrual Cycle Matters

The menstrual cycle is one of the most refined and subtle feedback systems operating in the bodies of human females. It can be helpfully understood as a cycle of seasonal changes, moving throughout the menstrual month: ovulation is high summer, whilst bleeding time is deep winter. Post-bleed, women move into springtime energy, whilst post-ovulation, women shift into the autumn harvest of pre-menstrual time.

We all know how dysfunctional we become when we do not get enough sleep. It is no different when a woman is out of synch with the natural rhythm of her menstrual cycle. The symptoms of interrupted sleep patterns, insomnia and jet lag are very like some premenstrual problems. We have been taught to see menstruality as a hassle, even a weakness that we need to pretend is not there. This creates a huge inner tension for women. Working against menstrual cycles can increase menstrual problems and infertility, dampen creative potential, distort relationships with each other and the natural world and censor the full authority of women's intuitive guidance systems.

Menstrual cycle awareness matters: it is the inner yoga of women (and the men who live with them), the ultimate self–care tool. As a stress-sensitive system, the menstrual cycle gives feedback physically and emotionally. By respecting and co-operating with its rhythm, we can experience greater levels of energy and wellbeing, creativity and productivity.

To practise yoga, informed by respect for cyclical rhythms and seasonal energy shifts, can help us to ascertain what practice best suits and supports us. Some days a high energy physical practice is just what is called for, and other days the most nourishing and strengthening practice would involve six bolsters, three blankets, a hot water bottle and plenty of total yoga nidra followed by a salt bath and a mug of tea… Refining somatic intelligence helps us to know what is being called for. And people who listen to the needs of their bodies are actually listening to the earth; that kind of listening is what is needed right now.

Dancing with Desire

We also need to learn to dance with our desires. The English word "desire" comes from the Latin *De Sidere*—of the Stars (connected to the English word sidereal). We are regularly told that desire is something to be pushed aside, to be transcended. But to be human is to desire. Our very lives are the desire of the Earth to produce us.

Instead of transcending desire, or becoming immune, or "solving" desire, the question is: how do we create an experience with our desires which empowers and enriches us?

Twenty-first century Daughters of Danu—Bealtaine Women and Girls Camp Practices   *Uma*

At Bealtaine *(May 1st) 2015, in South West Clare on the banks of the Shannon, eighteen women and seventeen girls between the ages of six and eighteen gathered for a Celtic Yoga celebration at Pure Camping eco-campsite. The practices included a meditative walk around the Loop Head Labyrinth, dedicated to Danu, the mother goddess of Ireland.*

Coming to the camp, all the women brought local honey from their homes in the four corners of Ireland, and from the north and west of England too. May morning dew, collected at dawn, was mixed with the honeys and with blackthorn essence to make a special kind of mead. A chalice of this mead was offered to each woman and girl as she entered the labyrinth, so she held the taste of that sweetness on her tongue as she journeyed to the centre to meet and honour the hidden goddess within her.

On arrival at the centre of the Labyrinth, each woman and girl sat for a moment with the resident statue of Danu, and then the younger girls ran out to receive chocolate at the exit from the labyrinth, and to dance and sing by the hedgerows full of blackthorn blossom.

Wild Nidras each day were shared in the cowshed that had been converted into a yoga studio, and all the yoginis snuggled up together, under blankets: mothers and daughters, sisters and friends. Every night one little eight year-old girl sat in the corner, writing in a book and apparently paying no mind to any of the yoga practices. But at the end of the retreat her mother, with permission from her daughter, brought the girl's poems to share, and her writings captured the spirit of burgeoning life and love that is the essence of Bealtaine.

The Love River

I am very soft

Feel me at the

End of each fingertip

I am always there.

Sunset over Black Head, Co Clare

Practice

Sun and Moon in the Breath

A subtle aspect of pranayama is *swara* yoga: the flow of breath in the nostrils. Left nostril is moon breath; right is sun breath. With awareness of rhythmic tides between the two nostrils' flows, we can follow the lead of moon or sun *swara*, or notice how certain movements and attentions change dominant nostril flow. This awareness is congruent with the wider perspective of Celtic yoga's seasonal observances, and heightens understanding of the dance between solar and lunar energies within our bodies.

If we track the breath's entries to and exits from the body, then we can also feel the passage from unity, through duality and back to unity; we can notice how the single vast ocean of air outside of us has to divide to move through the twin passages of the nostrils to enter our lungs, and then out again through the nostrils to return to the unity of air outside our bodies.

- *Blow your nose if necessary to clear blockages. Sit or lie comfortably, breathing easily through both nostrils.*
- *With each incoming breath, feel air moving up both nostrils in the triangle shape of the nose: the base of the triangle is the two nostrils and the tip is the bridge of the nose.*
- *Welcome air in the right nostril as solar flow, and air in the left nostril as lunar flow. Feel the movement of air through the two nostrils like the two sides of the triangle shape of the nose.*
- *At the height of the inhalation, feel the two streams of air merging into a single river at the top of the triangle of the nose.*
- *Welcome the natural flow of breath in the left (lunar) and right (solar) nostrils: notice the two separate streams of nostril breath merging at the top of the nose. Feel how these two flows become a single river of breath, moving deeper down into the body towards the lungs. How deep into the body can you track the entry of the breath?*
- *Exhaling, notice how the breath leaves from the lungs in a single river, moving up through the throat, and dividing into two streams of solar and lunar breath to exit through the nostrils.*
- *As breath leaves the nostrils and returns into open air, notice how the dual streams of sun and moon breath open out from the nostrils to become part of the single vast ocean of air outside. How far out from the body can you track the exit of the two streams of breath?*
- *Inhaling again, notice the ocean of air outside becoming two streams, dividing into sun and moon nostrils.*
- *As the inhalation reaches its height, notice the two streams of nostril breath merging to become one river as breath enters more deeply down into the body from the top of the nose.*
- *Exhaling, notice the single river of breath from inside dividing to become two streams of out-breath, travelling down through sun and moon nostrils; and then observe these two streams merging with the ocean of air as breath leaves the body.*
- *Notice the next three rounds of breaths in this way.*
- *Inhaling — one vast ocean of air outside becomes two streams of nostril breath, which meet at the top of the nose to become become one river of breath moving down into the lungs;*

⚜ *Exhaling — the one river of breath leaving the lungs becomes two streams, which flow into the ocean of air outside again.*

⚜ *Feel each breath move from unity, through duality, to unity, then back out through duality, to unity again. Breathe another three breaths like this.*

⚜ *Now notice which nostril is more open. Exhale strongly to feel which nostril expels more breath, or bring a hand close to the nostrils, feeling for the stronger flow. (If you discover there is balance, without a noticeably dominant side, then just choose one nostril as the "more open" one to proceed with the next part of the practice).*

⚜ *Rest your hands on your knees or in your lap. Bring attention to the dominant, more open nostril and flare it a little more open. Invite all of your breath to enter only that nostril, following the single stream of breath in the open nostril all the way up to the top of the nose. It is as if you were thinking your breath into one side only of the triangle in the nose, just up through a single nostril, the more open nostril.*

⚜ *Carry the awareness of the breath inside that single open nostril up to the very top of the nose, and then mentally guide the breath over the top of the triangle, and down and out through the other side of the triangle, the less open nostril. Flare the nostril a little more open as the breath exits through it.*

⚜ *Feel the breath leaving (how far out can you track its passage?), and then welcome the next inhalation back in, up through the nostril it just left, all the way up, to the top of the triangle of the nose, and then then mentally guide the breath over the top of the triangle shape of the nose, and down and out through the other, more open nostril.*

⚜ *One full cycle of this psychic sun-moon nose breathing brings you back to the starting point, to the more open nostril through which you first inhaled. Breathe effortlessly, as evenly as you can, in this pattern for three more rounds of breath, letting a single stream of breath move through sun and moon nostrils alternately.*

⚜ *Pause. Reverse direction and repeat.*

⚜ *Now return to noticing the movement of the breath in both nostrils, through the triangle shape of the nose: breathe three more rounds of breath through both sun and moon nostrils.*

⚜ *Inhaling—feel how the vast ocean of air outside you comes in through both nostrils, funnelling into the nostrils, dividing from the great single ocean of air outside of you, to become two streams, which merge at the top of the nose, becoming one river of breath entering more deeply inside the body. How far deep inside the body can you track the entry of the breath?*

⚜ *Exhaling—feel how the dual streams of sun and moon breath, one from each nostril, flow out from the bottom of the nostrils to become part of the single vast ocean of air outside. How far outside the body can you track the exit of the breath?*

⚜ *Let go of conscious attention to the breathing patterns, but retain awareness of the natural flow of breath in the nostrils as you go about your business today, breathing sun and moon in every breath.*

12 Asana—A Dance with Breath

The basis of our approach to the physical practice of yoga movements known as *asana* is rooted in the understanding of the body as a microcosm which reflects the macrocosm. The intention of the *asana* practice is to support the healthy function and relationship of the five elements in the body—earth, water, fire, air and space. At the same time we see it as a moving meditation, a dance with the breath, which integrates all of the five bodies—the physical, energetic, emotional and mental, intuitive and bliss bodies.

Celtic Yoga *asana* practice is always guided by breath awareness and a loving reconnection with the deep feminine energies of the Earth. Through well-grounded physical practice that roots us in the Earth, we can feel into naturally arising sensations. This experience is enhanced by poetry and music. It is offered in a manner that responds to and supports the fluctuations in the cycles of the body, the day, and the seasons.

The purposes of *asana* practice are many, and directed towards wellbeing, but their guiding light is to experience the true rapture of living and to become re-enchanted by our lives. The *asanas* are inspired by the power of a heart which has been awakened by the recognition that the great stories and myths of the Celtic world are our personal stories, the dreams that we share with our community.

Asana appears, on first sight, to be movement of the physical body, but, when practised with true awareness, the outer forms, shapes and movements radically affect the inner body, the energy body. These rhythmic and interlinked movements of energy are described in the *Tantric* tradition as the Dance of Shakti, but they can also be seen in the serpentine lines of the Celtic and pre-Celtic art of interlinked spirals, circles and other geometric forms.

Awareness is vital. The aim is for *asana* practice to become an intuitive dance. The physical movements are threaded on a focused breath so that the series of movements become so much part of the individual that, in the words of WB Yeats, "the dancer becomes the dance".

O body swayed to music, O brightening glance,
How can we know the dancer from the dance?

WB Yeats

Q: Can you teach yoga to a crow?
A: Crow is already doing upa yoga.

Q: What is upa yoga?
A: Attentiveness.
You are having a banana?
Crow is attentive.
He is wanting to see what's left... he is wanting to take the crumbs from your table.
He is not watching the news on television.
He is waiting for leftovers.
This is attentiveness.
Upa yoga!
Jains say this is best yoga.
Not standing on head.

Gabriel Rosenstock

Celtic Cross at Sunset in New York—the circles around the crosses represent the Cosmos

In the Indian tradition, energy is called Shakti, the feminine power of the Earth; consciousness is called Shiva, the masculine power of the Sun. One of the aims of *asana* in the Celtic School of Yoga is to practise in such a way that we bring energy to consciousness—Shakti to Shiva—through mantra, *asana*, *pranayama*, *mudra* and poetry.

Our bodies enjoy our practice in the same way that the Earth enjoys the Sun. Seasonal shifts in warmth and light evidently affect what form of movement is most appropriate at any given point in the cycle of the year. Lunar cycles and menstrual rhythms can also influence the nature of our physical yoga practice. There are many ancient sites in Ireland, such as Newgrange in Co Meath and Drombeg Stone Circle in West Cork, that celebrate the dance between Shiva and Shakti, the dance between the Sun and the Earth.

There is no set repertoire or series of prescribed movements that are specific to the Celtic School of Yoga; rather the teaching of *asana* welcomes sequences and poses from many different traditions of practice. The intention is for the practice of *asana* to be an enjoyable and fluid experience that arises from a respectful honouring and celebration of the flow of life through the body.

These dances were never exclusively Indian phenomena. Recent yoga scholarship by UK researchers Mark Singleton and Elizabeth de Michaelis has shown that the history of many of the *asanas* that we do in yoga incorporates Western ideas about body awareness and training. For example, the hybrid forms of *asana* practice we see in contemporary yoga were partially inspired by the physical training programmes of the British Army in India, and by other European body conditioning systems and Western positive-thinking and relaxation practices.

In the Celtic School of Yoga, *asana* is informed by an understanding that any time we work intelligently and responsively with the body, we are doing a multi-dimensional practice to express the pure joy of being human on this Earth.

Don't think the purpose of meditation is to go deep into consciousness, wrap a blanket around yourself, and say "how cozy! I'm going to curl up in here by myself; let the world burn."

Not at all. We go deep into meditation so that we can reach out further and further to the world outside.

Eaknath Easwaran

Faery Tree dancing in the stream of the wind, Connemara, Co Galway

Practice

Asana with the Triad Breath

This practice is based on triple rhythm. It can be adapted to almost any physical practice and helps to establish a meditative state within movement.

The principle is to listen to the natural sounds around us—such as rain on a window, a river flowing, waves lapping on the shore, leaves moving in the trees or even much longer cycles like the rising and setting of the Sun and Moon—and to listen for a slow triple rhythm within the overall symphony. Once this is established, take it as the base rhythm for your breath and move to it as if dancing to its music.

Once the tempo has been established let go of the initial input from nature—which has been a little like an orchestra tuning up—and bring your mind to the triple rhythm of your breath. This breath then itself becomes the music to which your body movements are attuned.

This following is a simple example but it can be adapted to any series of physical movements or asanas from any tradition:.

⚜ *Stand with your hands slightly away from your sides, palms facing forward, knees a little bent, and breathe normally.*

⚜ *Listen to the sounds around you until you can hear a slow triple rhythm. There is always something to listen for though it may not be obvious, or even audible, at first.*

⚜ *Synchronise your breath to this rhythm and breathe, one, two, three; one, two, three. Have a very gentle sound at the back of your throat (*ujayii*), just so you can hear the breath.*

⚜ *For a count of three breaths, move your arms above your head to about 45 degrees so that the movement is nicely in time with the breath and your hands reach their highest point at the end of the in-breath.*

⚜ *Turn your palms to face down and move your hands back to your sides for the out-breath.*

🔱 *Repeat this three times and then continue to any sequence of* asanas *using the breath as your guide. Once the rhythm has been established, let the counting go and move to the feeling or memory of it in your body.*

🔱 *Hold any* asanas *of your choice for three or five rhythmic in-and-out breaths and then proceed to the next one.*

🔱 *Always finish your* asana *sequence with resting for about ten minutes.*

13 Mudra and Bandha—Gestures and Locks

A *mudra* is a gesture and a *bandha* is a lock or seal. The gestures and seals of yoga work with the subtle anatomy of our physical and energetic bodies to welcome, direct and enhance flows of *prana*, the vital life force. To practise yoga with awareness of these locks and seals optimises our vitality. To practice yoga without attention to these locks and seals is depleting and effortful.

In the Celtic School of Yoga, we invite naturally arising *bandhas* to occur through breath, movement and awareness. Their observance and cultivation are an integral part of our practice. The experience of these gestures and seals is rooted in embodied knowledge of energetic pathways in the body. For example, when we pay proper attention to the way that our hands and feet, or the muscles of our pelvic floor, throat and respiratory diaphragms respond to the presence of energy in earth, air and sun, then we can consciously welcome vital force to enter our body's network of energy channels. This is nourishing and uplifting.

Working intuitively and subtly with the *mudras* and *bandhas* is like discovering how tides and currents flow in our particular stretch of water— our own body. With this understanding we can welcome these gestures and seals as spontaneous phenomena. Rhythmic pulsing of *mudra* with breath, and the observance and cultivation of naturally arising *bandhas* are integral to revitalising yoga practice.

Mudras include hand gestures for meditation and movement—for example, *Yoni mudra* (source gesture), *Hridaya mudra* (heart gesture), and *mudras* to balance each element. *Bandhas* include a diversity of pelvic locks and seals that respect gender difference and honour seasonal shifts and cyclic physical changes, for example a series of *Mulabandha* (root locks) specifically for men and women, with distinct variations for use during menstruation, menopause, postnatal recovery and pregnancy.

…the innocence of fragments is wise with us.
Keeps us from order that is not native to our dust.
Yet, without warning, a life can suddenly chance
On its hidden rhythm, find a flow it never knew.
Where the heart was blind, subtle worlds come into view;
Where the mind was forced, crippled thought begins to dance.

John O'Donohue

I exhausted myself looking.
Nobody ever finds this by trying.
I melted into myself, and came home.
Where every jar is full to the brim …
But no-one drinks.

Lalla

You won't find the Truth by crossing your legs and holding your breath.
You may dissolve in contemplation as the salt does in water
You may dissolve the salt in water but it won't become the sea.
Meditation and self-discipline are not all that's needed,
Nor even intense longing to enter the gates of freedom.
Because something more must happen.
Yes, something more must happen.

Lalla

Lia Fáil, the Stone of Destiny, Tara, Co Meath

Bandhas also include subtle lifts and locks in hands and feet, throat and abdomen, for example reclining abdominal and pelvic lifts that encourage vital energy to move freely through the physical, energetic and mental and emotional bodies. Such an integrated and holistic practice of *mudra* and *bandha* fosters an intuitive intimacy with sources of rapture and vitality.

Practicing yoga without *mudras* and *bandhas* is like sailing without paying attention to tides or winds: what could be effortless becomes difficult or impossible.

Just as a skilful mariner harnesses the forces of nature to sail his boat, so skilful *yogis* and *yoginis* use *mudras* and *bandhas* to direct subtle winds and tides of *prana* around their bodies. Both require awareness and a careful sense of timing cultivated through practice. High tides and strong currents of energy can move us with ease through poses (and through life), powered by naturally arising *prana*. A Celtic approach to yoga recognises the importance of *mudras* and *bandhas*, so that *prana* moves optimally through our network of energy channels.

Everything is new now for me.
My mind is new, the moon, the sun.
The whole world washed clean,
Washed in the rain of That.
Lalla leaps and dances inside the
energy of life.

Lalla

What Happens when we Hear the Music of what Happens…

Uma

To practise Celtic Yoga is to hear "the music of what happens". To do this calls for us to pay attention to what the body and breath has to say to us. Sometimes the body responds in the form of naturally arising locks and seals moving through the diaphragms of the body, lifting and redistributing energy.

When one day I gave myself permission to hear the "music of what happens", the act of paying proper attention to the songs my body was singing brought recognition and awakened awareness. Here is what happened when all the locks and seals arose spontaneously:

I was barefoot on the hill in the dawn, with wet grass and mud on my feet, fully grounded but expansive. A wave of energy moved up from the living Earth through my heart and into the top of my head. A second wave moved down from my heart and into the place where the root source (muladhara) and the fluid juice of the sacral energies (swadisthana) meet. Pure creative power (shakti), awakened in the form of loving energy in the heart space (hridayakasha), travelled at speed down to the source (yonisthana) and back up again, over and over.

The third and continuing wave reached up out of the Earth, and through my heart in concentric deep ripples of movement, each overlapping the previous wave, until the whole physical body was alive and in love with the rhythm of life. From the roots of each hair in my scalp, right down to the webs between my toes and fingers: each one of these places awakened and opened up in heat and space. My entire body was alive to the rhythmic gasps of vital breath as if fragments of life were being brought together into one coherent whole.

I have described these three waves individually, but they arose simultaneously, unwinding from a single, great, threefold, living rope of intertwined threads, like the trinity of pulsing vessels in the umbilical cord before it's cut from the placenta after birth.

The three threads are intelligence, love and pure power. The wave of intelligence moves upwards from heart to head, the wave of love shudders down from the heart, into the source (yonisthana) and back up into the heart, whilst the wave of pure power rolls out in rhythmic ripples from the heart space to the edges of the body and beyond.

The whole of this triple tide moves out in naturally arising locks and seals from centre to boundaries, into a pulsing field of awakened energy and intuitive knowing. These are not techniques to practise, they are gates to open, to meet the power of life herself.

Restorative and Therapeutic Yoga—Restoring the Rhythms of Power

Yoga is not just something we do when we feel good. It is a whole way of being, however we feel. We need rest as much as we need activity. This is the rhythm of power. To authentically nourish us throughout our lives, a yoga practice needs to respect the rhythms of power as they move through us. Usually the practice of restorative yoga involves propped static *asana*. This is good practice. But there is more to restoration than simply being still in a restorative pose. To truly nurture and restore the rhythms of power in all five bodies, we also need to come home to ourselves, to be grounded and nourished by the living earth, where we can be held by her and reintegrated at an elemental level in all of our bodies. Celtic Yoga shares a multidimensional practice of restoration that includes some or all of the following elements:

- Supported Restorative Poses
- Total Yoga Nidra
- Slow Rhythmic Movement
- Sound and Breath
- Poetry, Story and Music
- Being in Nature—a Relationship with the Earth

The form and structure of yogic restoration is as important as the form and structure of active practice. To maximise the beneficial effect of restorative yoga, the structure of practice can be modelled on the naturally arising process of retreat and restoration that occurs, for example, during menstruation when the wisdom of the body's cycles gifts women an inner retreat structured in the following way:

1. Separation
2. Surrender
3. Renewal
4. Vision
5. Clarity and Direction

The Song of Wandering Aengus

I went out to the hazel wood,
Because a fire was in my head,
And cut and peeled a hazel wand,
And hooked a berry to a thread;
And when white moths were on the wing,
And moth-like stars were flickering out,
I dropped the berry in a stream
And caught a little silver trout.

When I had laid it on the floor
I went to blow the fire a-flame,
But something rustled on the floor,
And someone called me by my name:
It had become a glimmering girl
With apple blossom in her hair
Who called me by my name and ran
And faded through the brightening air.

Though I am old with wandering
Through hollow lands and hilly lands,
I will find out where she has gone,
And kiss her lips and take her hands;
And walk among long dappled grass,
And pluck till time and times are done,
The silver apples of the moon,
The golden apples of the sun.

WB Yeats

Sanctuary in the Hazel Wood,
Colman's Cave, the Burren, Co Clare

Practice

Restoration

1. Separation: wash yourself clear with your voice

⚜ *Sit comfortably with eyes closed, breathe freely.*

⚜ *Yawn, free your jaw.*

⚜ *Bring the hands together at heart level, fingertips touching.*

⚜ *Hum as you move the palms of your hands up over your face, as if washing yourself with the sound of the hum.*

⚜ *Move your fingertips through your hair, over the top and back of your head.*

⚜ *Still humming cover your ears with the palms, feel the sound vibrations inside you.*

⚜ *At the end of the hum bring your hands back to your heart.*

⚜ *Repeat for as long as you enjoy.*

2. Surrender: let gravity love you

⚜ *Lay face down on your mat, or on grass, sand, rock, or earth. Turn your head to the side, pillowing with your hands if it is more comfortable.*

⚜ *Feel your belly resting on the earth, moving as you breathe.*

⚜ *With each exhalation, feel your whole weight settling down heavily into the earth beneath; breathe like this for as long as you like.*

⚜ *Be received by her.*

3. Renewal: receiving the power of life

⚜ *Roll gently onto your back, bend your knees, put the soles of your feet together.*

⚜ *Rest thighs on bolsters or cushions so the weight of the legs is held comfortably, at an easy angle.*

⚜ *Inhale, reach the arms up wide above your head, palms facing the sky.*

⚜ *Bend the elbows, relax the shoulders and rest elbows and backs of the hands on the earth. If necessary support wrists with cushions or blanket.*

⚜ *In this receptive position, allow every inhalation to bring vital energy into you.*

⚜ *With every exhalation, breathe little rootlets deep down into the earth, connecting with the living earth.*

⚜ *Be glad to be here, just breathing for as long as you like: every breath restoring energy and vitality.*

Practice

4. Vision

⚜ *Sit comfortably.*

⚜ *Bring palms together, rubbing until they feel warm.*

⚜ *Close your eyes.*

⚜ *Rest palms over closed eyes and feel warmth bathing the eyes.*

⚜ *Look and breathe into darkness in front of the closed eyes.*

⚜ *Open the eyes, look into the darkness and then open up spaces between the fingertips to let the light back.*

⚜ *Slowly lower hands, welcome colour and light into the eyes.*

⚜ *Repeat until your outer vision is refreshed.*

⚜ *Sit with eyes closed, see yourself in your mind's eye, here where you are now.*

5. Clarity and Direction

⚜ *Sit comfortably.*

⚜ *Bring hands to heart level, fingertips touching.*

⚜ *Exhale awareness down into your heart on every breath.*

⚜ *Let your attention settle in the heart space.*

⚜ *Be at home to yourself in the deep heart's core, and welcome into that space whatever guidance, insight, clarity or direction arises, or simply hold a space for future insights to arise.*

⚜ *Listen to the heart's own voice.*

⚜ *Speak or imagine the words:*
"With great respect and love, I honour my heart, my inner teacher".

Total Yoga Nidra, Nidra Shakti and Wild Nidra

Yoga Nidra is the queen of all relaxation techniques. It literally means "yoga sleep". It is a state of consciousness in which the body is asleep, yet the mind moves between alert attentiveness and restful trance states. References to *yoga nidra* can be found in Indian epic poetry dating back to 300BC, and in medieval yoga manuals from the first to the fifteenth century. These early references identify *yoga nidra* as a metaphor for the creative void, and as a state of profound freedom from conscious intentions. It is this aspect of *yoga nidra* that Yeats described so beautifully.

In early understandings of *yoga nidra*, the state is seen to be analogous to experiences of enlightenment that expand awareness beyond everyday limits. Since the nineteenth century, relaxation techniques that use elements of *yoga nidra* have inspired many western psychological approaches to relaxation, including self-hypnosis, mindfulness based stress reduction, and autogenic training. All these methods trace their roots to *yoga nidra*.

But *yoga nidra* is more than simply an ancient esoteric Indian philosophical concept. In the contemporary yoga world, yoga nidra is the fastest growing, most accessible and most effective form of deep relaxation.

In the Celtic School of Yoga, Total *Yoga Nidra* is an invitation to self-empowerment, a means of direct access to the meditative heart of yoga and an awakening of intuitive guidance. The intelligence of the practice meets the needs of the person who practises it, so it can offer healing and nourishment, creative inspiration, or spiritual insight, as appropriate. It is also a crucial means to reconnect human hearts to the living Earth. Total *Yoga Nidra* is a powerful force for change, for enabling humans to live consciously on this planet.

Nidra Shakti—or the Power of Repose—brings us into an experience of the creative void as a feminine force, naturally arising and utterly intuitive and free, like the very Earth herself. Awakening this *Nidra Shakti*—the spontaneous creative spirit of deep repose that connects each one of

Over and above the wood
The blue cuckoo chants to me
Dear Lord, thank you for your word
I write well beneath the trees

9th century Irish manuscript
(translated by Ciaran Carson)

Through states analogous to self-induced hypnotic sleep the devotee attains a final state of complete wakefulness... where the soul, purified of all that is not itself, comes into possession of its own timelessness.

WB Yeats

Wild Nidra on the
Burren pavement, Co Clare

us to the creative source—allows us to welcome the *nidra* practice our own being calls for, thus freeing us from the need for an external voice of guidance. If we embrace the loving roots of this practice, we are free to relish the beauty of the *Nidra Shakti* and to welcome our own intuitive knowing.

The experience of *Wild Nidra*—fully responsive *yoga nidra* practised in or near nature—also resonates and amplifies the spirit of place. In the Celtic School of Yoga we bring *yogis* and *yoginis* out into the land to have a direct encounter with the living creative spirit that can then emerge in *Nidra*. Yoga *Nidra* and naturally arising *Nidra Shakti* empower us to welcome the spirit of the living Earth within ourselves.

 Our quest for the greater world is a quest for a greater vision of the world we already live in.

John Moriarty

The Edge of the World,
the Cliffs of Moher, Co Clare

16 Spiritual Activism and Cyclical Awareness—Living our Yoga

To really know a person's yoga practice, you need to look at how they live in the world. Our new yoga paradigm is rooted and grounded in this earth and empowers practitioners to encounter the rapturous, living intelligence of the human body. An engaged yoga practice is a form of spiritual activism. If we share a practice that empowers people to learn to read the subtle signals of the human body, we are also empowering them to embody this experience as a vital part of the living earth.

To live our yoga with authenticity, we:

Leave no Trace
One aspect of a true yoga is accepting our ecological responsibility. This, for example, involves the practicalities of food politics—knowing where our food comes from, eating primarily organic and locally based foods, and realising how our choices impact on the planet.

Respect Rhythms and Cycles
All our human cycles can be understood to function in relation to seasonal patterns and energetic tides in the living earth. Awareness of such rhythms—for example menstruality, digestive rhythms and *swara* (the flow of the breath in the nostrils), patterns of sexual response, arousal and disinterest—is the basis of a yoga of cycles.

Recognise that we are a Microcosm
The global ecological crisis and the crisis in all aspects of human health have one and the same root—disconnection.

Support Community Involvement
Think global and act local—how not to be overwhelmed while taking practical steps towards ecologically responsible living.

The three most short-lived traces
The trace of a bird on a branch,
The trace of a fish on a pool,
The trace of a man on a woman.

An old Irish tré or triad

Leave this chanting and singing and telling of beads!
Whom dost thou worship in this lonely dark corner of a temple with doors all shut?
Open thine eyes and see thy God is not before thee!
He is there where the tiller is tilling the hard ground and where the pathmaker is breaking stones.
He is with them in the sun and in shower, and his garment is covered in dust.

Rabindranath Tagore

The sharing of a bad cup of coffee and a stale bread roll can be a real moment of blessedness. For Bloom, food is sacramental. While other Dubliners rush their meals or talk with their mouths full, he takes care of every culinary detail. At his lunch, he cuts his cheese sandwich into slender strips and he follows his action with a whole page of personal thoughts before eating it. Ulysses proceeds by the same almost Tantric sense of full presence...

Declan Kiberd, Ulysses and Us

At the top of Abbey Hill, the Burren, Co Clare

Now is The Needed Time

So many people are disconnected and depleted right now, seeking anywhere and everywhere for anything that promises to help them feel whole and at home. Even the journey of yoga has the capacity to take us out of ourselves, to draw us away from the very roots to which we need urgently to return.

Now is the time that, in each place on the earth and for each community, a place-specific and regionally responsive expression of yoga practice can emerge. The authentic practice of yoga is spiritual activism. From it evolves a living sense of ecological responsibility. This holistic practice of yoga not only enables the evolution of individual consciousness, but supports social and cultural transformation through grassroots community and global activism.

This new paradigm of yoga can be truly transformative, because it is not caught up in the hierarchies of control and submission to authority that have characterised many previous traditions of yogic teaching.

Sharing a life-affirming, accessible yoga practice, free from hierarchical power structures and exclusive teachings, recovers our deep, intuitive knowing. Trust is nourished by a genuine and rooted connection with the living earth, and by a living, but hidden, lineage of *yogis* and *yoginis*, who lived according to their hearts' truth, inspiring real change in our world.

Yogis from this hidden lineage include WB Yeats and his boyhood hero, Henry David Thoreau, writer, eco-activist and advocate of civil disobedience. *Yoginis* include the Irish educator and campaigner for Indian independence and women's rights, Sister Nivedita, and writer and philosopher Annie Besant.

Yeats is one of the first poets of de-colonisation because his poems are part of a search for authenticity ("Romantic Ireland's dead and gone") ... a search for a more congenial national origin than that provided by colonial history, for a new pantheon of heroes, myths, and religions... enabled by the land.

Edward Said

Now is the time to know
That all that you do is sacred.
Now is the time to understand
That all your ideas of right and wrong
Were just a child's training wheels
To be laid aside
When you can finally live
With veracity
And love.
...Now is the time for the world to know
That every thought and action is sacred.
This is the time
For you to deeply compute the impossibility
That there is anything
But Grace.
Now is the season to know
That everything you do
Is sacred.

Hafiz

Love and do what you will.

Augustine of Hippo

Irish Yoginis, Activists in India:
Threads from the Hidden Lineage

Yeats himself never got to India, even though he had yearned to, from the time he first joined the Dublin Theosophical Lodge. But there were other Irish yogis who did, including a number of women who combined spiritual practice with political activism.

Leading Theosophist Annie Besant, whose parents were both Irish, spent forty years working in India. Inspired by the 1916 Easter Rising, Besant started the Indian Home Rule movement, and in 1917 she was elected President of the Indian National Congress. She so profoundly influenced the young Mohandas Gandhi, that Indian politician Sarojini Naidu observed: "Had there been no Annie Besant, there would have been no Mahatma Gandhi".

Besant was joined in 1915 by Roscommon suffragette, Gretta Cousins, who founded the Indian Women's Association, and became the first female magistrate in India. Like Besant, her spiritual vision underpinned political activism. As a campaigner for women's rights, Gretta had been imprisoned for throwing stones at 10 Downing Street, and she spent a year in jail in Bombay as a result of protesting against the British government's Emergency Powers.

Amy Carmichael was born in County Down and lived in India from 1895 until her death in 1951. Her inspiration to serve the needs of poor women and children stemmed from a spiritual awakening as an adolescent, which led to her work for women's health in Belfast, and then later in India, where she set up many homes for orphan children, and was pivotal in passing laws in India to protect children from prostitution.

Another Ulster yogini, Margaret Noble, travelled to Calcutta to study with her yoga teacher, Swami Vivekananda. As "Sister Nivedita", Margaret Noble was one of a wave of courageous and inspired Irish women who had rediscovered the power of yoga and went to India to learn more. As a spiritual activist who lived her yogic vision, Sister Nivedita's understanding of yogic philosophy was the inspiration for her radical desire to serve the needs of Indian woman both by providing education and healthcare, and by working towards Indian independence.

Nivedita understood that these philosophical, social and political projects were intimately connected, and she knew that improving the health, status and education of women was crucial to India.

Following on the heels of these four pioneering Irish yoginis was Dublin-born Mollie Bagot Stack, who studied yoga in India in 1912, and brought her vitalising "stretch and swing" classes to the Women's League of Health and Beauty in London in the 1920s. Mollie's exercises were a feminine re-working of movement sequences identifiable as an influence in the popular form of yoga that has come to be known as Ashtanga Vinyasa Yoga.

17 Ethics and Boundaries

We now need a new paradigm in yoga-teaching relationships, and in the institutions that support them.

It is possible for yoga classes, retreats and trainings to be well-held, safe spaces that respect individual encounters with yoga as an immensely transformative and liberating practice. The Celtic School of Yoga seeks to protect and nurture the experience of yoga practice, and offers an open forum for the discussion of issues which have often been swept under the carpet. The intention of the school in respect to ethics and boundaries is to provide a practice environment in which students and teachers can feel nourished and free to explore the many aspects of personal and spiritual deepening that yoga can offer, safe in the knowledge that the emotional openness and trust that is often part of such deepening, will always be honoured and respected.

Students and teachers from all traditions are warmly welcomed to the Celtic School of Yoga's retreats and gatherings, or to contribute to the School's unique open forum discussions and colloquia on pertinent issues in yoga practice. Whenever necessary and appropriate, space and time can be given to hearing and honouring people's experiences with a view to providing healing through yoga community support firmly grounded in the ethics of clarity, honesty, kindness and truth.

The ancient Irish believed truth was sacred. In Irish and Hindu tradition, both of which come from a common ancestor, the formal pronouncement of truth is a magical act. In Irish it was *Fir Flathemon*; in Sanskrit *Satya Kriya*.

Come, come, whoever you are,
Wanderer, worshipper, lover of leaving.
It doesn't matter.

Ours is not a caravan of despair.
Come, even if you have broken
your vows a thousand times.
Come, yet again, come, come.

Rumi

God is good but the devil is not too bad
if you get to know him.

Irish Saying

Krishnamurphy in Love
Is there no one whom you do not love?
No, none at all.

What about the devil?

He most of all—if he exists—
Is in need of love

Gabriel Rosenstock

Women, Ireland, and Colonialism

In ancient Ireland, under Brehon law, women had far greater rights than in most of Europe; for example, as owners of land and property. These laws were accommodated within the new Christian laws, but still remained some of the most radical in Europe in terms of the legal equality of the sexes. The early Irish church was constantly in trouble with Rome because of these laws—radical Irish bishops at the Ecumenical Council of Macon in 900 CE were also responsible for defeating (by a single vote majority) the proposed decree that women had no souls.

The Seanchas Mór *(the great collection of old laws of Ireland) were preserved in copies made by the early Christian monks and priests. During the time of the Penal Laws, they were hidden, buried and smuggled from place to place, because to be found with a copy in your possession incurred the death penalty. Just as the established religious* kyriarchy *had attempted to quash the equality of the sexes recognised by the early bishops, so did the British empire attempt to eradicate all memory of the old Irish respect for women's civil and legal rights.*

Practice

Letting the Breath Cycle Reveal
Boundaries and Liminal Spaces

The sound of our own natural breath can be a deep comfort and a source of profound insight. Each breath offers us the chance to recognise the presence of cycles, limits and boundaries. If we are conscious of the rhythms of our breath, then every time we breathe we can sense more clearly how to welcome all that is naturally arising as it shifts across and between limits.

There is a whole day in every breath, a whole year in every cycle of inhale, exhale and the pauses between. These cycles teach us all we need to know about observing boundaries and limits.

   As the inhalation arrives, we welcome the vital energy carried into us on the air as a dawning morning light. It's the Spring of the breath cycle. When the air that was outside moves inside, we can track the place where what was public becomes private. The liminal space between inside and outside is crossed by the in-coming breath.

   In the pause after breathing in, we can notice the fullness of noon in the day of the breath cycle, when brightness is at its height and we are replete with the Summer of the breath. The natural capacity to retain the breath inside reaches its limits; we sense when we need to let go, and wait until we reach that edge.

   As exhalation leaves, the light of the breath's day fades and afternoon turns into evening. This is the breath's Autumn. We can consciously release all that is being carried out from us on the warm air. We can feel what was deep inside us moving out into the world. As we sense this movement, the boundary between the invisible inner world and the outer world is crossed by the outgoing breath.

   In the pause after the exhalation has left, we settle into the Winter night of the breath's cycle. There is nothing to be done but to rest and wait. Our intimacy is now with emptiness, not with fullness. When the desire to breathe in returns, we once more welcome the arrival of the dawning brightness of the next day's breath.

   Cultivating observance of the seasonal shifts of our own breath can teach us about the importance of liminal spaces, and heighten our appreciation of the need to respect boundaries.

18 Community—Satsang

Gatherings of *yogis* are called *satsang* in Sanskrit. This useful term literally means being with the truth (*sat*–true; *sanga*–company). In yoga circles, *satsang* is often understood to mean listening to the sermons of a *guru*. It can also be profoundly experienced as a sharing of our understandings of what is true and what is real. This is a vital part of living yoga. If we want to bring yoga to life as an everyday support for being human, and as a means to awaken consciousness of our relationship with the living Earth, then the company of other *yogis* and *yoginis* is a necessity. Celebrating the delights and recognising the challenges of being together in yogic community is at the heart of a Celtic approach to sharing yoga.

The Celtic School of Yoga *satsang* warmly welcomes all practitioners and teachers of yoga, regardless of lineage, tradition, affiliation, or levels of experience. The intention of our gatherings is to hold a conscious space of welcome for everyone with an interest in the practice of yoga as enchantment, rediscovery and transformation.

Icham of Irlaunde
Ant of the holy londe
Of Irlaunde.
Gode sire, pray ich the,
For of saynte charite,
Come ant daunce wyt me
In Irlaunde.

I am of Ireland
And of the holy land
Of Ireland
Good sir, I pray thee
For holy charity
Come and dance with me
In Ireland

Anonymous, 14th Century, in Middle English translated to Modern English

Don't torture this body with thirst and hunger,
Give it a hand when it stumbles and falls.
To hell with all your vows and prayers:
Just help others through life,
there's no truer worship.

Lalla

Sceilig Mhichil, Co Kerry

Co-creating a Celtic Yoga Gathering

Uma

In Corcomroe Abbey in 1998, together with the poet/ philosopher/priest John O'Donohue, we created a blessing ceremony for our marriage. The ceremony was a natural expression of the integration we felt between the spirit of the place and the yoga experience we had encountered.

The form of the ceremony arrived to me through yoga nidra *and dreams. I dreamt it so vividly that it was as if I was watching something that had already happened. We blessed the elements, brought water from the sea and the lakes, and then my seven year old cousin danced a jig over the gravestones in pure delight. And just at the point when we blessed the union, a pair of swifts soared high above the Abbey and into the sky. John O'Donohue let out an enormous laugh and talked about the lilies of the fields and the birds of the air.*

The rings were passed around through everybody's palms. A golden thread, that had been wrapped around a big chunk of old driftwood from the beach, was unwound and held by each pair of hands as the rings were threaded through. Each person placed a blessing from their heart, through their hands and into the rings. The gathering and the symbolic actions were integrated, elemental and nourishing.

This kind of creative and naturally arising ceremony binds sangha, *creates community and is, I feel, at the heart of the future of yoga* satsang— *connection and integration made manifest in simple gestures and conscious action. This is the living meaning of ritual, a beating heart of expressive loving connection, rhythmic and alive, in the body of the community.*

These kinds of ritual are not hollow or empty, they are the lived enactment of dream-visions, and their symbolic power is a natural and healing balm. This ceremony in Clare was a Celtic twin echo of an Indian ceremony to celebrate the spiritual union of Ireland and India in the form of Sita and Ram, the individual soul and the cosmic consciousness in 1997.

In the Deep Heart's Core
Yeats, Thoreau and Yoga on the Lake Isle of Innisfree

"I went to the woods because I wished to live deliberately, to front only the essential facts of life, and see if I could not learn what it had to teach, and not, when I came to die, discover that I had not lived. I did not wish to live what was not life, living is so dear; nor did I wish to practise resignation, unless it was quite necessary. I wanted to live deep and suck out all the marrow of life..."

Henry David Thoreau, Walden; or Life in the Woods, *1854*

The Lake Isle of Innisfree

I will arise and go now, and go to Innisfree,
And a small cabin build there, of clay and wattles made;
Nine bean rows will I have there, a hive for the honey bee,
And live alone in the bee loud glade.

And I shall have some peace there, for peace comes dropping slow,
Dropping from the veils of the morning to where the cricket sings;
There midnight's all a glimmer, and noon a purple glow,
And evening full of the linnet's wings.

I will arise and go now, for always night and day
I hear lake water lapping with low sounds by the shore;
While I stand on the roadway, or on the pavements grey,
I hear it in the deep heart's core.

WB Yeats, 1888

When Yeats was a boy, his father read aloud to him passages from Henry David Thoreau's account of yogic life, Walden; or Life in the Woods. *He loved the book and was so much enchanted by it that, years later in his autobiography, he recalls how he "… had the ambition, formed in Sligo in my teens, of living in imitation of Thoreau on Innisfree, a little island in Lough Gill."*

As a young man living in London in 1888, Yeats's recollection of his childhood love for Thoreau, and his adolescent ambition to live just like him out in the woods, led him to write The Lake Isle of Innisfree, *which he describes as "my first lyric with anything in its rhythm of my own music". The inspiration for the poem came to him out of a deep yearning for home.*

The yearning for a simple, yogic life, and a direct connection with nature, is a shared inspiration that clearly and directly bridges Yeats and Thoreau. This link is a thread in the forgotten yogic lineage that connects radical thinkers and poets, such as Thoreau and Emerson and Yeats, with those Indian philosophies that inform the practice of yoga.

Thoreau described himself as a yogi: "Depend upon it that, rude and careless as I am, I would fain practice the yoga faithfully . . . To some extent, and at rare intervals, even I am a yogi." Thoreau was just as enchanted by the "stupendous and cosmogonal philosophy" of the Upanishads *and the* Bhagavad Gita *as the young Yeats was enraptured by Thoreau.*

And just as Thoreau loved to "bathe his intellect" in the Mahabharata, *so too, throughout his life, Yeats's own "… endless research into life, death, and God" brought him over and again to the study of Indian philosophy. He read the* Yoga Sutra *in his twenties, and although he loved the idea of the yogis meditating out in the woods, he was frustrated for years by the formal language of academic and scholarly editions of Patanjali. "I want to hear the talk of those naked men…" he wrote, in his introduction to Sri Purohit Swami's* Aphorisms of Patanjali, *expressing his relief that at last, he had met an authentic yogi, someone who knew yoga "in his bones". It was Sri Purohit Swami who finally satisfied Yeats's youthful desire to experience, at least vicariously, the yoga he had been reading about all his life. But in his deep heart's core, Thoreau always remained the poet's first, and much beloved, yoga teacher.*

19 Afterword—What Next?

This *Aisling*, our bright vision or dream of a Celtic School of Yoga, presents a new paradigm for the practice of yoga. It is a poetic manifesto, thoroughly rooted in and responsive to the land and the communities of people who live upon her.

The Celtic School of Yoga is an invitation to the growth of a yoga that is rooted and enraptured, welcoming and inclusive, awake to the present politics of the world, yet able to nourish our dreams through a connection with the past. From one side of the Indo-European expansion to the other, it is through renewed honouring of the presence of the land and cycles of life that a respectful connection with power can be re-established.

Perhaps this vision resonates with you? Perhaps you feel as if reading this book, you recall something from a long way back or from deep within yourself? Perhaps you too share this vision of a yoga that is local and appropriate, that feeds our bodies and our souls, right here where we are planted?

If the emergence of such a yoga feels needful and timely to you, then we look forward to welcoming you to The Celtic School of Yoga, so that together we may explore a new paradigm for the future of yoga practice that is nourished by what we bring from the past, from the places in which our families have lived, and in whose soil we have grown.

Our cycle of retreats, gatherings and trainings each year includes many seasonally attuned opportunities for different forms of *satsang*, including joyful summer camps, winter celebrations by the fireside, training groups, more intimate retreats for smaller gatherings, and one-to-one sessions which focus on particular aspects of practice or philosophy that are of current relevance in a practitioner's life cycle.

The long-term vision for the Celtic School of Yoga is to support the growth of grass-roots local gatherings, apprenticing, mentoring and on-going professional and personal development as part of the relationships supported by a community of teachers, trainers and practitioners. In addition to the rhythm of such gatherings, online communities can provide support and learning opportunities both for students who are attending courses and retreats, and for those who are unable to attend in person.

We invite you to join us.

www.celticschoolofyoga.com

Glossary of Sanskrit Terms

Ashtanga Vinyasa yoga: flowing form of athletic yoga sequences taught by Pattabhi Jois.
Apana: downward moving energy.
Bandha: a lock, or binding bond.
Bhakti: heartfelt spiritual devotion.
Brahma: the creator god.
Buddhi: discriminative intelligence.
Chakra: literally wheel, or vortex, metaphorically a spinning energy centre.
Danu: water goddess.
Deva: a god.
Devi: a goddess as a general term, or as a suffix, eg. Lakshmi Devi.
Guru: literally "heavy", generally understood as a teacher.
Hanuman: monkey god, embodiment of courage, devotion and intelligence.
Hatha: literally "forceful", generally referring to physical yoga practice.
Hrid/Hridaya: (spiritual) heart.
Hridaya mudra: heart gesture.
Hridayakasha: space of the spiritual heart.
Kali: the black goddess.
Kamala mudra: lotus gesture.
Kosha: "sheath", layer or covering, referring to different aspects of existence.
Krishna: god of love, music and poetry.
Kundalini: coiled energy in the first chakra, envisioned as a sleeping snake.
Lakshmi: goddess of abundance, consort of Vishnu.
Mahavidya: great wisdom, great wisdom goddess/es.
Manas: mind.
Mantra: "instrument of thought" i.e. sound or words containing the energy of spiritual transformation.
Mouna: inner silence.
Mudra/s: gesture.
Mulabandha/Mula bandha: root lock, vaginal/perineal lift.
Nadi: (long i) river.
Nadi: (long a and long i, retroflex d): tube or channel through which prana, the energies of the physical, subtle and causal bodies flow. There are over 1008 of these channels in the energy body.
Namaskar/a/am: greeting
Namaste: greeting with palms touching, signifying "the divine light in me greets the divine light in you".
Nidra: sleep.
Nidra Shakti: power of repose.
Patanjali: author of the *Yoga Sutra*, earliest written codification of yoga philosophy.
Parvati: consort of Shiva, the mountain goddess.
Prana: life force.
Prana shakti: the power/energy of the life force.
Prana vayu: the life force in the form of breath, or "wind".
Pranamaya: full of prana, or life force; that dimension of being that is to do with energy.
Pranayama: expansion or extension of the life force through the extension and conscious control or "dancing" with the breath.
Puja: ceremonial or ritual worship (simple or complex), done with devotional attention to honour deities or elemental forces.
Santosa: the happy acceptance of what arises; contentment as a spiritual discipline.
Sati: Siva's first wife (also meaning a virtuous woman).
Shakti: energy, power, strength or ability.
Shakti pith: places in India where the body of Sati is believed to have fallen to earth.
Shiva: the "beneficent" or "kindly one"; the god of destruction and lord of yoga.
Surya namaskara: sun salutation.
Sutra: thread, verse.
Swadisthana: "one's own place or abode"; second chakra, located in the pelvis.
Swami: "boss" or "lord", honorific for renunciate.
Swara: flow of air breathed through the nostrils.
Tantra/s: texts or doctrines, also with the meaning "loom, fibre, or weave".
Tantrik /Tantric: to do with tantra.
Tantrika/Tantrikas: practitioner of tantra.
Tapas: disciplined ascetic effort, austerity, heat.
Tara: "star" (f), one of the great wisdom goddesses, also with

the meaning "crossing over" (m).

Tattva: element, essence or substance.

Ujjayi: victorious breath.

Upanishad/s: "to sit near", philosophical texts, the last part of the Vedas.

Veda: ancient Indian scripture.

Vedanta: the "end of the vedas", Indian philosophical system.

Vinyasa: sequenced flow.

Yoga: union.

Yoga nidra: the sleep of the yogis, or the yoga of sleep.

Yoga Sutra: literally "threads of yoga", series of aphorisms on yoga.

Yogi: one who practices yoga (male).

Yogini: one who practices yoga (female), also a supernatural being.

Yoni: source, origin, vulva, vagina, womb. Also home, or place of rest.

21 Bibliography

Aldhouse-Green, Miranda. *The Celtic Myths: a guide to the ancient gods and legends*, London, 2015.

Augustine of Hippo, 'Homilies on the First Epistle of John', Translated by H. Browne. From *Nicene and Post-Nicene Fathers, First Series*, Vol. 7. Edited by Philip Schaff. Buffalo, NY, 1888. Revised and edited for New Advent by Kevin Knight: www.newadvent.org.

Avinson, Jo, *Yoga: Fascia, Anatomy and Movement*, Pencaitland, 2014.

Blake, William, edited by N John McArthur, *William Blake: The Complete Illuminated Books*, London, 2000.

Brown, James, *A Companion to James Joyce*, Chichester, 2011.

Campbell, Joseph, *The Power of Myth,* New York, 1988.

Carson, Ciaran, 'The Scribe in the Woods', in *The Finest Music, An Anthology of Early Irish Lyrics,* edited by Maurice Riordan, London, 2014.

Chesterton, GK, *Tremendous Trifles*, Start Publishing USA, 2013 (1909).

Condren, Mary, *The Serpent and the Goddess*, London, 1991.

Danaher, Kevin, *The Year in Ireland*, Dublin, 1972.

Dickinson, Emily. Ed Johnson, Thomas H. *The Complete Poems*, London, 1990.

Dinsmore-Tuli, Uma, *Yoni Shakti: A woman's guide to power and freedom through yoga and tantra,* London, 2013.

Dinsmore-Tuli, Uma, *Mother's Breath*, London, 2006.

Scotus, Johannes (John the Scot) and Jean A Potter, *Periphyseon on the Division of Nature*, London, 2011.

De Beauvoir, Simone, translated and edited by H M Parshley, *The Second Sex*, London 1997 (1949).

De Michelis, Elizabeth, *A History of Modern Yoga: Patanjali and Western Esotericism*, London, 2005.

de Paor, Louis, editor, *Celtic Book of Days*, Dublin, 2007.

Dillon, Myles, 'The Hindu Act of Truth in the Celtic Tradition', in *Modern Philology,* 44: 137-40, 1947.

Dillon, Myles, *Celt and Hindu*, Osbern Bergen Memorial Lecture, Dublin, 1973.

Doidge, Norman, MD, *The Brain's Way of Healing - Remarkable Discoveries and Recoveries from the Frontiers of Neuroplasticity*, New York, 2015.

Dumézil Georges, translated by Alf Hiltebeitel, *The Destiny of a King*, London, 1988.

Easwaran, Eaknath, *The Upanishads*, Tomales, CA, 2007 (1987).

Fiorenza, Elisabeth Schussler, *Wisdom Ways: Introducing Feminist Biblical Interpretation*, Maryknoll, NY, 2001.

Gershon, Dr Michael, *The Second Brain - A Groundbreaking New Understanding of Nervous Disorders of the Stomach and Intestines,* London, 1998.

Gimbutas, Marija, *The Gods and Goddesses of Old Europe, 7000 to 3500 BC: Myths, Legends and Cult Images*, London, 1974.

Gladwell, Christopher, *Engaged Yoga*, Siddha Yoga Publishing, Bristol, 2014.

Gladwell, Christopher, 'Lines of Flow' downloaded from http://www.christophergladwell.com/wp-content/uploads/2014/04/lines-of-flow.pdf September 2015.

Graves, Robert, *Greek Myths*, Volume 1, London, 1984 (1955).

Hafiz, translated by Daniel Ladinsky, *The Subject Tonight is Love – 60 Wild and Sweet Poems of Hafiz,* London, 2003 (1996).

Hanna, Thomas, *Somatics: Reawakening the Mind's Control of Movement, Flexibility and Health*, Cambridge, 1988.

Hoskote, Ranjit, *I, Lalla: The Poems of Lal Ded*, New Delhi, 2011.

Kanduri, C, et al. 'The effect of music performance on the transcriptome of professional musicians', in *Nature*, March 2015.

Kapur, Narinder, 'Four Irish Ladies in India' in *The Irish Raj: Illustrated Stories about Irish in India and Indians in Ireland*, Antrim, 1997.

Keown, Daniel, *The Spark in the Machine - How The Science of Acupuncture Explains the Mysteries of Western Medicine*, London and Philadelphia, 2014.

Kiberd, Declan, *Ulysses and Us: The Art of Everyday Living*, London, 2009.

Kibler, William W. (trans). *The Elucidation* (or the Rape of the Well Maidens), for The Camelot Project from the edition by Albert Wilder Thompson, *The Elucidation: A Prologue to the Conte del Graal,* New York: Publications of the Institute of French Studies, Inc., 1931. http://d.lib.rochester.edu/camelot/text/elucidation

Kinsella, Thomas, editor, *New Oxford Book of Irish Verse*, Oxford, 1986.

Kubjika tantra, in *Kubjika the erotic goddess: sexual potency, transformation and reversal in the heterodox theophanies of the Kubjika Tantra*, Mark S G Dyczkowski, downloaded 28 September 2015 from http://www.indologica.com/volumes/vol21-22/vol21-22_art08_DYCZKOWSKI.pdf

Lalla, translated by Coleman Barks, *Naked Song*, Varanasi, 2006.

Lalla, translated by Ranjit Hoskote, *I, Lalla: The Poems of Lal Ded*. New Delhi, 2011.

Langevin, H, M, "Connective tissue: a body-wide signaling network?" *Med. Hypotheses*, 66:1074–1077 (Epub Feb 17), 2006.

Lawrence, DH, *Lady Chatterley's Lover*, London, 2013 (1928).

Lennon, Joseph, *Irish Orientalism: A Literary and Intellectual History*, Syracuse, NY, 2004.

Matthews, Caitlin, *Celtic visions: seerships, omens and dreams of the otherworld,* London, 2012.

Macalister, RAS, *Lebor Gebala Eireann*, Dublin, 1938. Online index at http://www.ucc.ie/celt/indexLG.html

Mallory, JP, *The Origins of the Irish*, London, 2013.

McKillop, James. *Dictionary of Celtic Mythology*, Oxford, 1998.

Moriarty, John, in *Dreamtime Revisited,* a film by Dónal Ó Céillechair, Anú Pictures, 2012.

Myers, Tom, *Anatomy Trains*, New York and Philadelphia, 2014 (2001).

Ó Catháin, Seamus, *The Festival of Brigit: Celtic Goddess and Holy Woman*, Dublin, 1995.

Ó Crulaoich, Gearóid, *The Book of the Cailleach—Stories of the Wise-Woman Healer,* Cork, 2003.

Ó Hogáin, Daithi, *Myth, Legend and Romance: An Encyclopaedia of Irish Folk Tradition,* New York, 1991.

Osho, *Zorba the Buddha: Talks given from 1/1/79 to 31/1/79 Darshan Diary,* 1982. Downloaded 28 September 2015 from http://osho.netai.net/Zorba%20The%20Buddha.pdf

O'Donohue, John, 'The Burren Prayer' and 'Assumption', in *Conamara Blues*, London, 2001.

O'Donohue, John, *Benedictus: A Book of Blessings*, London, 2007.

Oliver, Mary, 'Mysteries, Yes', in *Evidence,* Boston, 2009.

Paul, Russil, *The Yoga of Sound: Tapping the Hidden Power of Music and Chant,* Novato CA, 2006.

Pert, Candace, *Molecules of Emotion: Why You Feel the Way You Do,* New York, 1998.

Porges, Stephen W, 'The polyvagal theory: phylogenetic substrates of a social nervous system' in *International Journal of Psychophysiology,* 42 (2), 123-146, 2001.

Rosenstock, Gabriel, *The Pleasantries of Krishnamurphy: Re-vealations from an Irish Ashram,* Salisbury, 2011.

Rumi, translated by Coleman Barks, *Rumi: The Book of Love: Poems of Ecstasy and Longing,* New York, 2003.

Said, Edward, *Nationalism Colonialism and Literature: Yeats and Decolonization,* Field Day Pamphlets, Derry, 1988.

Schleip, R et al, *Fascia - The tensional network of the human body.* New York, 2012.

Siegel, Daniel J, *The Pocket Guide to Interpersonal Neurobiology - An Integrative Handbook to the Mind,* New York and London, 2012.

Singleton, Mark, *Yoga Body: The Origins of Modern Posture Practice,* Oxford, 2010.

Sjöö, Monica, and Mor, Barbara, *The Great Cosmic Mother: Rediscovering the Religion of the Earth,* San Francisco, 1987.

Slavin, Michael, *The Ancient Books of Ireland,* Dublin, 2005.

Stephens, James, *Irish Fairy Tales,* 1920, downloaded 28 September 2015 from http://www.gutenberg.org/files/2892/2892-h/2892-h.htm

Stiles, Mukunda, *Yoga Sutras of Patanjali,* San Francisco, 2001.

Tagore, Rabrindanath, *Gitanjali, Song Offerings, a collection of prose translations from the original Bengali,* London, 1913.

Tagore, Rabrindanath, *Some Songs and Poems* translated by Pratima Bowes, Shantiniketan, 1984.

Teasdale, Wayne, Foreword to Russil Paul, *The Yoga of Sound,* qv.

Thoreau, Henry David, *Walden, or life in the Woods,* Oxford, 2008 (1854).

van der Kolk, Bessel, MD, *The Body Keeps the Score: Brain, Mind and Body in the Healing of Trauma,* New York, 2014.

Waddell, John, *Archaeology and Celtic Myth: An Exploration,* Dublin, 2014.

Wei Wu Wei, *Open Secret,* Hong Kong, 1982 (1965).

Walker, Barbara G., *The Women's Encyclopaedia of Myths and Secrets.* London, 1986.

Yeats, WB, and Shree Purohit Swami, *The Ten Principal Upanishads,* London, 1975 (1937).

Yeats, WB, 'Introduction' to *Gitanjali, Song Offerings, a collection of prose translations made by Rabindranath Tagore from the original Bengali,* London 1913.

Yeats, WB, *Selected Poetry,* London, 1974.

Yeats, WB, edited by W H O'Donnell, *The Collected Works Volume V: Later Essays,* New York, 1994.

Index of Practices